SAHNISH (ARIKARA)
ETHNOBOTANY

CONTRIBUTIONS IN ETHNOBIOLOGY

CONTRIBUTIONS IN ETHNOBIOLOGY

Marsha Quinlan and Justin Nolan, Series Editors

Contributions in Ethnobiology is a peer-reviewed monograph series presenting original book-length data-rich, state-of-the-art research in ethnobiology. It is the only monograph series devoted expressly to representing the breadth of ethnobiological topics.

Explorations in Ethnobiology: The Legacy of Amadeo Rea
Marsha Quinlan and Dana Lepofsky, Editors

Sprouting Valley: Historical Ethnobotany of the Northern Pomo from Potter Valley, California
James R. Welch

Secwepemc People and Plants: Research Papers in Shuswap Ethnobotany
Marianne B. Ignace, Nancy J. Turner, and Sandra L. Peacock, Editors

Small Things Forgotten: Artifacts of Fishing in the Petén Lakes Region, Guatemala
Prudence M. Rice, Don S. Rice, and Timothy W. Pugh

Ainu Ethnobiology
Dai Williams

Sahnish (Arikara) Ethnobotany
Kelly Kindscher, Loren Yellow Bird, Michael Yellow Bird, and Logan Sutton

Sahnish (Arikara) Ethnobotany

Kelly Kindscher, Loren Yellow Bird, Michael Yellow Bird, and Logan Sutton

Society of Ethnobiology

2020

Library of Congress Control Number: 2020906467

ISBN 978-0-9990759-2-0 (paperback)
ISBN 978-0-9990759-3-7 (PDF)

Society of Ethnobiology
Department of Sociology & Anthropology, University of Puget Sound
1500 North Warner St., CMB#1092, Tacoma, WA 98416

Cover photo: From top left and then clockwise:

1) SteštAhkáta "Yellow Corn Woman", also called Snow, an important source of information for Melvin Gilmore and his research on the Arikara (Sahnish) Ethnobotany. She was a midwife and basketmaker and artist, who was 83 when he interviewed her and took this picture in 1923 on the Fort Berthold Reservation in North Dakota. Here she is making baskets with two children seated next to her. National Museum of the American Indian, Smithsonian Institution, Catalog Number NO8708.

2) A chokecherry (*Prunus virginiana*) pounder. This tool was used to crush chokecherries, pits and all, for use in corn mush, or dried to be used in many foods. Melvin Gilmore purchased this tool from (Tawísa', *She Comes Back*) Mrs. Redtail, in August 1923. National Museum of the American Indian, Smithsonian Institution, Catalog Number 12/2093.

3) A fish trap made by White Bear (KuuNUxtaaká) required many specific plant species for its making: sandbar willow saplings (*Salix exigua*) for the fencing, four strong ash (*Fraxinus pennsylvanica*) posts, a cottonwood (*Populus deltoides*) pole for the center, white sagebrush (*Artemisia ludoviciana*) was used for purification and to ward off any human scent on the trap, and baiting it with maggot-infested rotten meat (tsaskoótu'). In addition, a root of red baneberry (*Actaea rubra*) must be on hand as it and sandbar willow bark are applied and rubbed into any catfish "stinging" (spine wounds). The photograph was by Melvin Gilmore, at the edge of the Missouri River on the Fort Berthold Reservation in 1923. Catfish were regularly caught and shared when the fish trap was used. National Museum of the American Indian, Smithsonian Institution, Catalog Number NO8741.

4) The prairie turnip or tipsin (the Lakota name that Gilmore encouraged us to adopt; *Pediomelum esculentum*) was a major wild food across the Great Plains, and gathered by Arikara woman. But, because the Arikara were so skilled at growing corn, they usually traded for the roots, especially from the Lakota, or other tribes. These braided strings of peeled roots show the thick, swollen portion that was used as food, in sauce, soups, or stew. The tougher, narrow root portion allowed them to be braided. This string was purchased by Melvin Gilmore in 1923. National Museum of the American Indian, Smithsonian Institution, Catalog Number 12/2999.

Table of Contents

List of Figures

Acknowledgments

The most important acknowledgement is to the Arikara people and to those who shared their traditional knowledge with Melvin Gilmore. They included (and dates when known): Betsy Boy Chief 1923, Cedar Woman 1923, John Box 1924, Mrs. Butcher 1923, Dawish (**Tawís**, short for **Tawísa'**, "She Comes Back") or Mrs. Redtail 1923, Crow Ghost (**KaakaaneekAsaánu'**; tobacco informant), Frank Hart (**NeétAhkas TiiriwátAt**, "Rising Eagle") 1931, William Deane 1931, Mrs. Mary McCauley, Julia Red Bear 1923, Albert Simpson (**KuúNUx KananiikatariíNU**, "Slow Bear") 1926, White Bear (**KuuNUxtaaká**) 1923, Clare Everett 1923 (who was educated at Carlisle Indian School and interpreted for Gilmore), and perhaps most importantly (for the depth and amount of information), Stesta-kata (**SteštAhkáta**), also called Yellow Corn Woman or Snow, Yellow Bird (**NikUstAhkáta**) 1926. We also need to acknowledge Fred Fox, tribal representative of the Eastern segment of the Fort Berthold Reservation and the members of the Tribal Council of the Three Affiliated Tribes, for their support of this project.

Douglas Parks, Professor Emeritus of Anthropology and Associate Director of the American Indian Studies Research Institute (AISRI), Indiana University, recorded plant knowledge and names from numerous Arikara consultants with whom he worked to document the language, from 1970 to 2001. Those cited in this manuscript include Ella Waters, William Deane, Jr., Alfred Morsette, Angela Plante, and Lillian Brave, although many others contributed to the documentation of the language, permitting this reevaluation of Gilmore's notes and manuscript. All of these speakers are owed great and sincere gratitude for their contributions, whether they offered only a few words of their language or hundreds of hours of narratives and lexical elicitation. It is thanks to their efforts that we are able to expand on Gilmore's documentation of the Arikara names of the plants he recorded. Dr. Parks' notes were supplemented with preliminary binomial nomenclature and notes by Sally Anderson, whose efforts have greatly facilitated correlations between Gilmore's and Parks' notes.

Much of the work of compiling, database entry, and editing occurred at the University of Kansas and included those associated with the Kindscher lab including: Rachel Craft, Amy Isenberg, Jessica Lackey, Leanne Martin, Natasha Myhal, Bob Rankin, Maggie Riggs, and distinguished editor, Deborah Wagman. In addition, Mary Adair, Senior Curator and the KU Biodiversity Institute provided helpful editing and critique.

In addition, the following archives below were visited by Kindscher and provided invaluable access to their historical resources regarding Melvin Gilmore and his work. Tom Mooney, Curator of Manuscripts at the Nebraska State Historical Society, helpfully offered help to their Gilmore-related archives. At the State Historical Society of North Dakota, Emily Schott, and then Emily Ergen, Archives Specialists, helpfully provided me access not only to

Melvin Gilmore archives, but also to those of George Will, who was his best friend and colleague throughout later part of his research career.

Richard Ford, Professor Emeritus, Anthropology and Curator Emeritus, Museum of Anthropological Archaeology, University of Michigan was well-known by Kindscher in the ethnobotanical research world, and as a curator was the first person that was approached about completing this Gilmore manuscript regarding Arikara ethnobotany, and after he retired he provided invaluable perspective on Gilmore's work and the University of Michigan archives. Karen Dively and then Lauren Fuka, Collections Managers, respectively, for Museum of Anthropological Archaeology, University of Michigan were helpful in finding Gilmore resources in the Museum, as was Carla Sinopoli, Professor Emerita, Anthropology; Curator Emerita. Most of Gilmore's manuscripts and papers have been transferred from the Museum to the Bentley Historical Library, at the University of Michigan, where Malgosia Myc, Assistant Director for Reference and Academic Programs, was very helpful in finding and then accessing these resources.

Gilmore conducted some of his most important work at the Heye Museum in New York City. This important collection was transferred to the Smithsonian Institution's collections in the Washington D.C. area. These collections included not only papers and material goods, but also photographs used in this manuscript. Heather Shannon, photographic archivist at the Smithsonian Institution, Suitland, MD, now photography curator at George Eastman House, Rutgers University, was exceptionally helpful in providing access to these materials. Also, Pat Niefeld, Supervisory Collections Manager, National Museum of the American Indian, Suitland, MD and Adam Minakowski, Reference Archivist, National Anthropological Archives, Smithsonian Institution, Suitland, MD also provided invaluable assistance in accessing these collections in order to get copies of important manuscript information and archived notes.

And finally, the photographs in the manuscript come from many sources and are all greatly apprecaited. The plant images in order of number are from Kelly Kindscher, Michael Haddock, Matt Lavin, Craig Freeman, Peter Dziuk, Katy Chayka, Robyn Klein, Rachael Liester, Steven Norris, Ernie Marx, D. Herman, and Jennifer Moody. The photos by Melvin Gilmore are in the Smithsonian collections and have been made available with Reference Archivist, Nathan Sowry. The maps of the ranges of each species are from Kartez (2015) and we want to thank them for permission in making them available. The map of the Arikara territory was made by Hannah Redford.

Section 1.

1. Overview

The Arikara, or more accurately "Sahnish," are a northern Great Plains tribe currently living on the Ft. Berthold Indian Reservation in central North Dakota, whose cultural history includes the growing a number of different varieties of corn, beans, and squash, and practicing other means of horticulture. They also acted as "middleman" traders of their surplus crops and Euro-American goods to other tribes, as well as hunting and using wild plants of the central and northern Great Plains. We review their use of the wild plants which have not previously been brought together from a tribal perspective. From historical accounts we have uncovered 106 species from 31 plant families that have specifically been used for food, medicine, craft, and other uses. Much of the information we obtained and analyzed was from the field notes and manuscripts of ethnobotanist Melvin Gilmore, who studied and recorded Arikara ethnobotany from 1916 to 1935. Gilmore worked extensively with Arikara people when he curated for the North Dakota Historical Society (1916–1923) and visited them frequently through1934 while at the Heye Museum in New York, and then the University of Michigan. He interviewed elders, collected material goods, and wrote a short draft manuscript on Arikara ethnobotany, but was not able to finish his work due to a debilitating illness. His manuscripts, papers, and field notes that we used are archived at the Nebraska and North Dakota State Historical Societies, the University of Michigan archives and Anthropology Museum, and the Smithsonian Institution.

In addition, we gleaned historical accounts of Arikara plant use from the journals of Great Plains explorers, including Lewis and Clark, John Bradbury, Pierre Tabeau, and others. Also, linguist Douglas Parks carried out extensive documentation of the tribe's language from 1970–2001 and from those interviews and notes more plant information was incorporated into this work. We have used all of these source materials to compile the current work for which botanical terms and plant names have been updated to the current botanical nomenclature and linguistic orthography. This work provides a partial recreation of Arikara ethnobotany and highlights the depth of the tribe's traditional uses of plants for food, medicine, crafts, utilitarian purposes, and other uses.

2. Introduction

The Sahnish (Arikara) were, and continue to be, an important tribe of the northern Great Plains (present-day North and South Dakota) whose ethnobotany has not been previously published. Our study provides details about the Arikara tribe, their original way of life, and their use of wild plants for food, medicine, and ceremonial purposes. We also provide background on Melvin Gilmore's ethnobotanical work, career, and his meticulous research and interactions with Arikara elders concerning their traditional use of plants. Gilmore's careful study of Arikara culture and ethnobotany from 1916–1934 included the collection of material goods for museums, detailed notations in his journals, and extensive writings. His focus on archiving materials has allowed us to complete the work that he began, to recreate the deep connection of the Sahnish and their plant world.

This publication's most important purpose is to stimulate interest among contemporary Arikara people, and other interested parties, to use this ethnobotany to understand how Arikara ancestors made use of the plants in their natural world and to explore the plants' implications for improving present-day health. Today, the Arikara and most other tribal groups in the United States face a number of health disparities. Some of the leading causes of death among American Indians and Alaska Natives, most of which are highly preventable, are heart disease, cancer, diabetes, and stroke (Heron 2017).

These Native groups also experience disparities in their mental health status: a high prevalences of depression, substance abuse disorders, suicide, and anxiety, including Post-Traumatic Stress Disorder (Beals et al. 2005). In the past Arikara people were unlikely to experience disability or death from the above illnesses, due to diets that were centered upon whole, domesticated and wild foods that contained appreciably higher levels of fiber, and contained significantly less sugar and refined carbohydrates. Other protective factors for the Arikara, among others, were no doubt a much higher level of activity as well as the therapeutic social benefits of village ceremonial life.

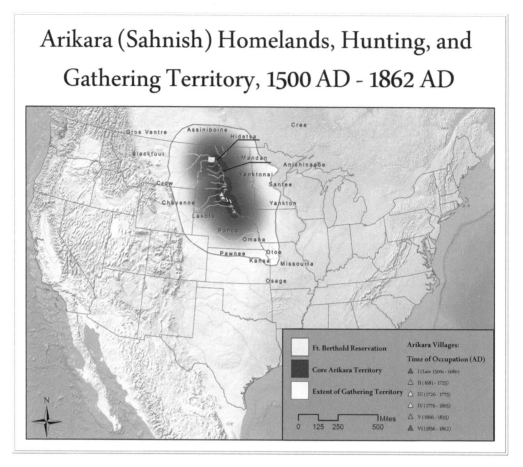

Figure 1. Before the Arikara Nation was forced onto the Ft. Berthold Reservation with the Hidatsa and Mandan Nations, they accessed an extensive territory surrounding the middle Missouri River region. The core Arikara Territory, in dark purple, is the most intensively used area, and is composed of land used frequently, up to 40 miles from their villages (Parks 2001). The village sites of the middle Missouri region show the most extensively used territory known and these are divided into six historical periods based on dated artifacts (Rogers 1990). The color of the village sites follow a migration south to north as the Arikara separated from the Pawnee and continued north until moving onto the Ft. Berthold Reservation. The furthest territory of use, in light blue, is the extent to which we believe they traveled to collect or trade for the plant species that the Arikara used. For this we used the geographic distributions of the plants that they collected (as seen in the maps for each species) and determined the boundaries of the land for which they could be collected from. Map created by Hannah Redford. Used with permission.

3. The Sahnish (Arikara) People

Arikara tribal members refer to themselves as "Sahnish" (*sáhniš*) which means "the people." They are also sometimes known as the "Ree," a shortening of "Arickaree", an old American name for the tribe. Tribal members use Arikara, Ree, or Sahnish to identify themselves. We use Arikara and Sahnish interchangeably in this work. The Sahnish have lived on the Northern Great Plains (in present-day North and South Dakota) for hundreds of years. The Arikara are members of the Northern Caddoan speaking group. It is thought that these groups came ultimately from what is now the southwest United States; Arikara elders have maintained an "out of Mexico" migration story, claiming that this is where the tribe originated.

In 2018, one of the authors, Dr. Michael Yellow Bird, an Arikara tribal member, used a genetic testing service to develop a deeper understanding of his personal genome and to explore his ancestry, heath, and relationships with his DNA relatives that have also used this testing service. He was also interested in whether they may be a slight possibility that he might have genetic markers that might support the Mexico migration story. Growing up his father, Willard Yellow Bird (deceased), always told him that their tribe had come from down south, probably South America. Yellow Bird's family tree identifies at least six to seven generations of Arikara ancestors on both his mother and father's sides. One of the reports provided is called Ancestry Composition, which is based upon a geographic analysis "that tells you what percent of your DNA comes from each of the 22 worldwide populations. It's based on the DNA you inherited from all your ancestors on both sides of your family."

He was stunned by the results which revealed that his ancestry composition included DNA matches with ancestors in Mexico and Central America: Michoacan, Jalisco, Puebla, Durango, Oaxaca, Zacatecas, Guanajuato, Nuevo Leon, Chihuahua, and Mexico City. Is this enough support for the out of Mexico theory? Maybe not. And, while the origin of the Arikara may not be from Mexico or Central America, according to Yellow Bird's DNA tests, there is certainly a possibility that this was a stopping point for the tribe.

Not long after the first genetic test, Dr. Yellow Bird submitted another sample of his DNA to another genetic provider that specializes in "Nutrigenomics," which is the study of the relationship between nutrition and a person's genes. "Nutritional genomics examines and analyzes how nutrients impact our genes, how our genes impact reactions to specific nutrients, and how our bodies may be struggling with dextoxing and metabolizing" (Darcey 2017).

His interest in doing this test was to determine not only how the results might inform his nutritional needs, but whether he could draw some connections to an Arikara horticultural lifestyle and an ancestral plant-based diet. The test determined that his overall macronutrient intake should be: 25% fats, 55% carbohydrate, and 20% protein. However, the tests revealed that the majority of these macronutrient calories should come from plant-based sources. Previously, he had followed the popular "Paleo" diet which focuses on foods that were assumed to be available to humans during the paleolithic era: meat (also organ meats), fish, vegetables, and fruit, leaving dairy and grain products out of the diet.

Interestingly, his genotype is more likely to do a good job of clearing blood sugar down to healthy levels after eating carbohydrates (yams, sweet potatoes, quinoa, wild rice, pumpkins, squash, carrots, and buckwheat, oats, and brown rice). Conversely, his test identified genetic risk variants associated with eating saturated animal fats which would elevate his risk of heart disease, obesity, and diabetes. The recommendation is that most of his fat calories should come from mono- and polyunsaturated plant fat sources such as avocado, nuts, seeds, and plant oils. Finally, his genes do best with plant-based sources of protein, for instance, lentils, black beans, hemp seeds, pinto beans, walnuts, and chickpeas. Small portions of pastured or wild poultry and wild fatty fish are acceptable. According to the test, it is optimal for him to avoid most dairy products, beef, pork, processed meats, and processed plant proteins such as tempeh. If he were to eat animal sources of fat such as grass-fed beef it is recommended that he eat only a weekly 4 oz. portion. In other words, "Animal sources of saturated fat should be reserved as a treat ... and plant foods as the staples" of his diet.

If Dr. Yellow Bird's nutritional genome is typical of present-day Arikara people and their past ancestors, then it makes sense that today's Arikara diet should largely be plant-based, low in saturated animal fats and protein, and similar to a traditional Arikara diet. Not surprisingly, a number of genes that have been tested show a strong relationship between saturated fat, obesity, diabetes, and heart disease, and lower polyunsaturated fat intake (Phillips et al. 2012). Today, the rates of diabetes, heart disease, and obesity among the present-day Arikara is much higher than that of the general population.

It is then no coincidence that the Sahnish lifestyle emerged through ties with traditional horticulture, living in earth lodges, and the development of a complex religious system centered on corn. Maize, integral in the Sahnish world and spiritual life, features a female deity called Mother Corn, the most beloved and honored figure of the Sahnish. In the origin story of the Sahnish emergence into this world, she led the people out of Mother Earth and gave them important teachings of how to live morally, courageously, and in balance with the rest of the world.

Through the past 150 years, the Sahnish people have endured a number of hardships, including disease epidemics, droughts, starvation, warfare, loss of lands and culture, being forced onto reservations, and by the US government asserting control of their destiny. But the Sahnish have persisted in the face of these disasters. The pressures experienced by the Sahnish marked the beginning of a change from the traditional lifestyle to contemporary living that has left the Arikara in a state of illness and "dis-ease" and grasping for survival. Ella P. Waters, a highly respected elder of the tribe who has since passed away, when reflecting upon the Sahnish condition remarked:

*TatanuuNUxtahnaawaaRUxtií'It   noohunaačituú'u'   niiniisuuxUhuu-
naawaanú sáhniš ačitaánu'. Táku' tiwekaneenuhneswaawiíšu'. Čituú'u'
nuuwenaaNItkaana'íWA niiniisuxteswaaWIšú.*

We had sacred ways—all the rituals that the Arikara tribe used to perform.
Now no one knows those ways. Now dust has covered all the old traditions
(Parks 1991a:1024; see Pronunciation Guide).

From ancient memory, oral traditions such as these, and information captured by various
historians, anthropologists, scholars, elders and members of the tribe, the Sahnish are reor-
ganizing and are beginning to revive some their older traditions, ceremonies, and language.
Younger members are working hard and collaborating with one another so the Sahnish will
not lose their culture. We are fortunate that *neešaánu' t'načitákUx na at'ná' waaRUxtií'u'*
("The Chief Above" and "Mother Corn") have brought members of the Sahnish forward who
are strong enough to continue recovering the Arikara ways, so when the time is right, many
Sahnish traditions will return and carry on.

4. The Arikara Microbiome and Medicinal Plant Use

The human microbiome, although only briefly mentioned in this work, may have a great deal to do with the health of both yesterday's and today's Arikara people. The microbes in the human digestive tract are referred to as the gut microbiome and are thought to play a critical role in both health and disease (Bull and Plummer 2014). Bacterial cells within the human gut outnumber human cells by more than 100 times.

> Imbalance of the normal gut microbiota have been linked with gastrointestinal conditions such as inflammatory bowel disease (IBD) and irritable bowel syndrome (IBS), and wider systemic manifestations of disease such as obesity, type 2 diabetes, and atopy [a tendency to develop allergies] (Bull and Plummer 2014).

Growing evidence strongly suggests that diet and lifestyle have important effects on our gut microbiota, which in turn influence our well-being. For instance, exercise appears to have an important influence on microbial populations associated with obesity, while sufficient levels of dietary fiber "may be the best way of maintaining a healthy gut microbiota population" (Conlon and Bird 2014).

What did the Arikara microbiome of the past look like? We can only speculate. But given the whole, natural foods that Gilmore reported Arikara ancestors consumed, it is very likely that it was much healthier and diverse. For instance, the seeds of sunflower (*Helianthus annuus*), the tubers of Jerusalem artichoke (*Helianthus tuberosus*), and the leaves and seeds of lambsquarters (*Chenopodium* spp.) and pigweed (*Amaranthus* spp.) are all good sources of protein and dietary fiber (Kindscher et al. 2018). Overall, the greens and wild fruits that were eaten would be considered "Super Foods" today; wild meats are highly touted for their leanness and low cholesterol content, and utilizing wild plants as medicine have also gained support from the public and the scientific community. In addition, recent research shows that new immigrants to the U.S. lose gut microbiome diversity as they start eating a modern Western diet (Vangay et al. 2018). We can infer that this was also experienced by the Arikara and other people in the Americas.

It is also interesting that Arikara children who ate ground cherries (*Physalis* spp.) were also eating clay found near the Missouri river. In doing so, they were very likely ingesting beneficial microbes in the soil and a number of essential minerals that may have been missing from their diets. Indeed, throughout the world humans have eaten clay to supplement a mineral-deficient diets. Some experts believe that geophagy, [the ingestion of clay and dirt], can have a number of health benefits (Lallanilla 2005). There are many other possible benefits from their ingestion which need more research, with the protection from toxins and pathogens being one that is currently favored (Young 2010; Young et al. 2011).

What does the Arikara microbiome look like today? Given the numerous inflammatory and chronic diseases of the population, such as obesity and diabetes, it is very likely that present day Sahnish have an unhealthy imbalance of gut microbial populations. It may be that by returning to eating a number of the diverse, traditional wild foods and plants of the past, the microbiome of the Arikara tribe will improve, as will the health of the people.

Along with food and its original nutritional status, we know very little about traditional medicinal plant use. We do know that medicine was more holistic than the Western pharmacological view in which chemical compounds are applied to affect bodily functions, and that spiritual practices and larger perspective contributed to healing as well. But even the Western world view was so narrow and limited in its scope that there was not a close look below the surface of Arikara medicine, health, and healing systems. The observation by John Bradbury on June 14, 1809, when visiting the Arikara villages along the Missouri River, gives us a small glimpse into some plants that had medicinal uses:

> I walked with Mr. Brackenridge to the upper village, which is separated from the lower one by a small stream. In our walk through the town, I was accosted by the Medicine Man, or doctor, who was standing at the entrance of a lodge into which we went. It appeared that one of his patients, a boy, was within, for whom he was preparing some medicine. He made me understand that he had seen me collecting plants, and that he knew me to be a Medicine Man or doctor, who was standing at the entrance of a lodge into which we went. He frequently shook hands with us, and took down his medicine bag to show me its contents. As I supposed this bag contained the whole material medica of the nation, I examined it with some attention. There was a considerable quantity of the down of reedmace, (typha palustris) [most likely *Typha latifolia*] which I understood was used in cases of burns or scalds; there was also a quantity of a species of artemisia, common on the prairies, and known to the hunters by the name of hyssop; but the ingredient which was in the greatest abundance was a species of wall-flower; in the character it agrees with cheianthus erysimoides [*Erysimum asperum*]; besides these, I found two new species of astragalus, and some roots of rudbeckia purpurea [*Echinacea angustifolia*]. After examining the contents of the bag, I assured the doctor it was all very good, and we again shook hands with him, and went into several other lodges, where we were very hospitably received (Bradbury 1904).

5. Sahnish (Arikara) Linguistics

Arikara belongs to the Caddoan language family. It is thus related to Pawnee, Kitsai, Wichita, and Caddo, a family that by the late Precontact period extended from the central Arkansas-Texas border through West Texas, Oklahoma, Kansas, Nebraska, and into the Dakotas. All of these languages except Kitsai are known to have been dialectally diverse, and it is these dialectally distinct bands that are often mentioned in the historical records up until the modern period. Thus, Caddo is the amalgamation of the Hasinai, Hainai, Kadohadacho, Natchitoches, and Yatasi, while Wichita consists of Waco, Tawakoni, and Wichita Proper—and the federally recognized Wichita Tribe absorbed the remaining Kitsai speakers in the late nineteenth century. Pawnee was historically divided into four distinct bands, the Skidi (Skiri), Chawi, Kitkehahki, and Pitahawirata, while the latter three—known collectively as the South Band(s)—all spoke the same dialect in contrast to the Skiri. The Arikara tribe historically were divided into 12 villages, many or all of which probably spoke a distinct dialect. Of all this original diversity, only the Pawnee dialect distinction survived into the late twentieth century to be rigorously documented. Earlier dialect distinctions among the other groups largely survived only through idiosyncratic differences among individuals or families.

Within the Caddoan language family, Arikara is most closely related to Pawnee. Indeed, it is only through a few minor and regular—but pervasive—sound changes that the two languages have become mutually unintelligible. Given the linguistic closeness, and the close historical relationship it reflects, Pawnees and Arikaras regularly visited each other even after the beginning of the reservation period, well into the twentieth century. As an example, Gilmore learned that his main Pawnee consultant, White Eagle, was visiting Fort Berthold in 1918, even though he was in his 80s.

Despite being neglected by early ethnographers in comparison to other nearby and related tribes, the Arikara language had been well documented by the beginning of the twenty-first century, when the last of the most fully fluent speakers passed away. This documentation began in the early 1900s, when Reverend Charles L. Hall and tribal member Ernest Hopkins translated a Christian catechism and several hymns into Arikara in an effort to introduce literacy to the tribe. The next significant study of the language wouldn't be until the latter half of the twentieth century, when linguist Allan Taylor recorded a few short stories from Lottie Webster in 1961. This project has been continued in earnest by Douglas Parks from 1970 until until his recent retirement. Parks had begun his doctoral research on Pawnee in 1965 and also continued that work until recently. At the same time, he has studied the Arikara language, which was greatly facilitated by his work with the Pawnee. In the course of 30 years, he worked with over two dozen Sahnish speakers, recorded and transcribed over 150 historical and mythological narratives (most of which were published in Parks 1991a), and collected thousands of lexical items across numerous semantic domains. Since 2006, linguist

Logan Sutton, along with other students and staff under Parks' supervision, have been expanding, compiling, and analyzing Parks' Arikara and Pawnee materials towards publishing comprehensive dictionaries and other reference materials for the languages. While a couple of other linguists have made some study of Arikara, the data collected by Parks remains by far the richest and most extensive.

Melvin Gilmore's ethnobotanical research among the Arikara ended before the language had begun to be analyzed using twentieth century linguistic methods. Despite this, Gilmore's notes suggest that he had a good ear for the sounds of the language and a meticulous method for recording what he heard. However, he also clearly did not attain proficiency in the complex grammar of the language or the exact composition of the plant terms he collected. The format of his handwritten notes suggests that any literal and compositional interpretations of Arikara terms that he recorded were interpolated from comments provided by his consultants, but that Gilmore did not have sufficient linguistic knowledge to critically evaluate these comments. But, his transcriptions and notes are sufficient in most cases for a modern linguist familiar with Arikara to interpret the words that Gilmore recorded. Gilmore's notes thus provide a rich, but only minimally tapped, linguistic resource for botanical vocabulary in Arikara. Several terms that he collected were not elicited from fluent speakers by Parks or other later linguists, and some differ from later elicitations in subtle morphological details that reflect the older generation and the greater familiarity of Gilmore's consultants with the plant names.

As mentioned, the last fluent speakers of Arikara passed away in the early 2000s. Several elders today retain passive knowledge of the language and can remember words and phrases when reminded, but much of the more nuanced and detailed vocabulary, such as the botanical terms represented in Gilmore's notes, are not remembered. However, there is a continued urgency to safeguard traditional wisdom, to honor traditional knowledge, and to find ways to re-invigorate the use of native plants by traditional people, especially among the youth. Fortunately, there are several tribal members who have dedicated themselves to learning the language based on the written and audio recorded materials that were collected in the course of the twentieth century and there is a renewed interest among the younger generations in reviving and revitalizing the language and other cultural knowledge at risk of being lost.

6. Melvin Gilmore and His Work on Arikara Ethnobotany

Figure 1. Melvin Gilmore, as Director of the Ethnobotanical Laboratory at the University of Michigan. Undated photo from the early 1930s, Box 3, Melvin R. Gilmore Papers, Bentley Historical Library, University of Michigan.

Melvin Gilmore (1868–1940) was a pioneering ethnobotanist who wrote over 90 publications in the course of his career. He studied, published, and recorded field notes on the ethnobotany of the following tribes: Arikara, Dakota, Lakota, Ojibwe, Omaha, Osage, Oto, Pawnee, Ponca, Potawatomi, and Winnebago. He was born in Valley, Nebraska, and as a child he grew up near the last Pawnee village to contain earth lodges and in the vicinity of the recently created Omaha and Winnebago Reservations. He lived on the farm well into his adulthood until he enrolled at Cotner College in Lincoln, Nebraska. Here, he developed his interest in native culture and native plants. He recognized that the original tribal lore and traditional ecological knowledge would be lost as native tribes moved from traditional lifestyles to much more limiting reservation life. He served as curator at the Nebraska Historical Society and, while employed there, also worked on his Master's thesis at the University of Nebraska study-ing the ethnobotany of the Omaha, which he published four years later (Gilmore 1913a). He next worked on his PhD. dissertation, which he completed in 1914 at the age of 46. Over the next few years he modified and published his dissertation as *Uses of Plants by the Indians of the Missouri River Region*, a Smithsonian Institution, Bureau of American Ethnology, 1918 report. It has subsequently been republished many times and is his most well-known work (Gilmore 1977).

Also in 1914 he accompanied White Eagle, a Pawnee elder, to east-central Nebraska and recorded information from him about many abandoned Pawnee village sites. White Eagle gave him his name "Pahuk" [*Paahaku*], which was also recognized as his Indian name later by the Arikara. *Paahaku*, meaning "Hill on the Water", is the name of a sacred Pawnee site near Fremont, Nebraska, a bluff overlooking the Platte River that was said to contain a mythical lodge where different animals would hold council. White Eagle also visited Gilmore at Ft. Berthold during one of the frequent personal visits between the Pawnee and Arikara. In 1916, Gilmore became curator at the State Historical Society of North Dakota in Bismarck, and for the next seven years he developed an abiding interest in and relationship with the Arikara people on their reservation. Gilmore greatly appreciated Arikara culture and its use of plants and natural products and this sparked his keen interest in learning more. The elders—both older women and men—who he interviewed were not just sources of information, they became the voices for it. He traveled to visit them by train and later by car, especially after he took his next position with the Heye Museum (now part of the Smithsonian Institution) in New York City in 1923, when he started making long summer road trips back to Nebraska and North Dakota, and when he had substantial funding for travel. He was fascinated by Arikara culture and made considerable effort to record their lore and, with Heye Museum funds, paid his Arikara collaborators for translations and cultural items, many of which he contracted for their construction. These included baskets, tools, toys, bags, parfleches, bows and arrows, moccasins and traditional dried foods, pots, dried fruits, teas, and plants used in ceremonies. These and other items are very significant cultural artifacts in the Smithsonian Institution collections. He also recorded children's games from the Arikara and other tribes, believing that other Americans should adopt such games in order to connect people with their bioregions and natural environments. It was his profound interest in, and honor for, the Arikara people and their uses of plants, and ceremony, that created a safe space for the knowledgeable Arikara—usually elders, and often women—to share gems of their wisdom that Gilmore was able to record.

Gilmore was a careful researcher. For example, in his notes taken on the Ft. Berthold Reservation in 1923, he recorded the following: "The Arikara name of the 'fish medicine,' ~~which until further identification I believe to be~~ is now identified as *Actaea arguta* Nutt., is *skanikaatit*." This later strike-through shows his repeated work on the manuscript and his careful attention to identification (NMAI Box 196, Folder 10). Also, he was very keen on plant species identification and 40 of his herbarium vouchers remain at the University of Michigan Anthropology Department (most are from work with the Lakota; only two are from his Arikara work). In viewing his specimens, almost all appear to be identified with the correct names used in his time. In addition, he collected food products, basketry, teas, and other materials which contain plants that he specifically identified. All of these are archived and reference is made to these materials among the plants listed below.

Gilmore produced over 25 publications containing Arikara cultural content, but many of his notes were never published. As Gilmore began work at the University of Michigan, he had a series of illnesses and he also was diagnosed with Parkinson's disease. As his health declined, he could not even complete a trip back home from a visit to the Arikara in 1934, as a serious bout of illness left him in Fergus Falls, Minnesota unable to drive any further. He had to have his understudy, Volney Jones, drive up to Minnesota to rescue him and return him to Ann Arbor, Michigan where he could convalesce from what would be his last Arikara visit (correspondence with George F. Will, Sr., in Will Family Papers, State Historical Society of North Dakota; also Melvin R. Gilmore Papers, Box 1). One of his greatest regrets was that he could not complete the Arikara work in North Dakota and, as he stepped down from his faculty position at the University of Michigan, he pleaded with long-term anthropological friend and seedsman, George Will of Bismarck, ND to finish his Arikara work and he requested that Volney Jones send Will some of his most important materials (correspondence in Volney H. Jones Papers, 1942, Box 1). When Jones sent the materials, he also stated that it was too bad that Gilmore did not finish the Arikara ethnobotany and that it would take considerable work to do so. Unfortunately, Will did not publish anything related to the Arikara materials that were sent to him. It is that work, the completion and interpretation of Gilmore's ethnobotanical notes, which we are completing, not only to honor Melvin Gilmore, but especially to honor the Arikara people who shared their intimate and profoundly insightful traditional ecological knowledge.

7. The Arikara Ethnobotany Manuscript and Notes

This project is intended to be of mutual interest to ethnobotanists, historians, and Sahnish People. It is not just a list, as it contains detailed cultural notes and information. When Melvin Gilmore began his work with the Arikara (Sahnish) soon after he took the position of Curator of the North Dakota Historical Museum in 1916, he made the acquaintance of many Arikara people and got to know some of them quite well. He continued his work by making summer visits after taking his next curator position at the Heye Museum in New York in 1923. The majority of his field notes on plant uses are from 1923–1926.

Gilmore's methodology was to meet people, get to know them, and informally interview them. He was especially interested in meeting Arikara elders because he was most interested in the old ways, the cultural practices and uses of plants before reservation life. He often camped at the Fort Berthold Reservation and wrote George F. Will Sr. about his July 10, 1923 visit:

> I have seen a number of my people and have sent out word to others. Everything seems to be favorable and I hope to get some results. In fact I have already today picked up a few new items of information. Snow says she is willing to make the baskets for me. I have seen Mrs. Red-tail and she says she will go out and get some clay and do the pottery for me. I have heard of some who can make bulrush matting. Claire Everett says White Bear can make a fish trap if I want him to. Red Bear told me about a number of articles. One of these is a deer decoy call made from bark. He says he will make it for me. Before I had been in camp long enough to go and gather wood for my fire Bear's Belly came driving up to my camp with some wood and, though he can speak no English, he made me understand the wood was for me (Will Family Papers, Box 3, Folder 23).

When he met people, he visited with them and subsequently gained their trust. This work was often slow and time-consuming. From his written notes while visiting the Arikara on July 24, 1928, he stated:

> I could not seem to accomplish much today. In the morning I wrote a report to Mr. Heye. Then I went up to see Mrs. Redtail about the pottery work, but there was no one there to interpret for us. She seemed anxious to do whatever she could. She got some clay out and broke up some stone for tempering, and then she kneaded the clay and pounded stone for me to see. She sent a small boy running to bring a schoolgirl from a neighbor's place over the hill. But the girl was not able to talk much. Mrs. R said she would

go after the Deanes to come over and interpret, and could come back at 6 pm. So I came back to camp and got dinner, then I went over to Everett's, but I found him away and his mother sick, and Mrs. Sittingbear gone visiting. So there was nothing to do there. I came back to camp and ate a cold lunch to make ready to go back to Redtail's. When I got there I found Mrs. Redtail anxious again because Deanes had gone to Elbowoods and were not yet back. After waiting till 7pm I started away, but before I had gone far the Deanes arrived and called me back. But it was too late to start in now, so it was agreed I should come back in the morning and the Deanes' older daughter would be there to interpret (Will Family Papers, Box 3, Folder 23).

Once he began working at the Heye Museum, Gilmore had funds to purchase cultural artifacts, transactions he discussed with artisans above. He paid people to make traditional pottery or purchased dried chokecherries that they would process for him and describe. This also led him to then purchase a very old chokecherry maul that was used to crush the dried seeds and pits.

Gilmore wrote in field notebooks, where he kept the information he learned about the plants, including the scientific name, common name, Arikara name, and edible, medicinal, and other uses. Later, after he was hired to establish the University of Michigan Ethnobotanical Laboratory in the Anthropology Department, in 1929, he put the plant names and their uses onto file cards (first in longhand but later re-typed), and created an archive for them there. Later he turned his notes into manuscripts and there are many drafts of his published and unpublished manuscripts in all four major archives. He also wrote a 7600-word manuscript entitled "Some Aboriginal Uses of Plants by the Arikara Indians", archived at the Bentley Historical Library at the University of Michigan (Gilmore 1932). This document describes 51 plant species with their uses and subsequently is responsible for many entries that follow. Gilmore's specific text in these instances is followed with a (G) in the text below. In addition, he published some important articles related to Arikara ethnobotany. The most interesting was based on interviews of Arikara women including the elder SteštAhkáta "Yellow Corn Woman", also called Snow, who was 83 when he interviewed her in 1923 about issues related to childbirth and gynecology. It was remarkable that they were willing to share details of their practices with a man, although SteštAhkáta also stated that: "in olden times complications of pregnancy were uncommon." This was due to many factors, such as the skill of the midwives, including SteštAhkáta, and the general excellent health of Arikara women. This information led to Gilmore (1931a) publishing "Notes on the Gynecology and Obstetrics of the Arikara Tribe of Indians".

He also published many other small papers of ethnobotanical interest containing Arikara ethnobotany including works on native tobaccos, *Nicotiana quadrivalvis* Pursh (Gilmore 1922), the ground bean or American hog peanut *Amphicarpaea bracteata* (L.) Fernald

(Gilmore 1925a), cattails, *Typha* spp. (Gilmore 1928) and the silverberry, *Eleagnus commutata* Bernh. Ex Rydb (Gilmore 1927a). He also published on plants used in Arikara fish traps (Gilmore 1924a), in Arikara basketry (Gilmore 1925b), in "Arikara Commerce" (Gilmore 1926a), and in stories, such as the "The Coyote's Boxelder Knife" (Gilmore 1927b), as well as in his wonderful book of Native American stories, *Prairie Smoke* (Gilmore 1987). But as discussed, Gilmore's Arikara work remained unfinished due to his illness.

8. The Process of Compiling Gilmore's Notes and Manuscripts

Gilmore's manuscripts, papers, and field notes were archived at the Nebraska and North Dakota State Historical Societies, the University of Michigan Bentley Historical Library archives, and Anthropology Museum, and the Smithsonian Institution's Archives (both National Museum of the American Indian and the National Anthropological Archives) in Suitland, Maryland. Kindscher visited all of these archives and recorded notes, photocopied, and photographed materials (manuscripts, correspondence, notebooks 1918 diary, and etc.) for use, which totaled about 5000 pages of material for further study. All of the materials were categorized and put into a spreadsheet database categorized by: plant species, tribe, date, source of material, institution, with whom Gilmore corresponded, uses, description of content, and other topics of interest. We used these materials and his other publications to compile the current work, which provides a partial re-creation of the Arikara ethnobotany with edible, medicinal, craft, and other uses. Besides the notes and papers on ethnobotany, Gilmore had also gleaned information on animals, Native American agriculture, cultural practices, ceremonies, and many other topics. Also, the Smithsonian Institution—in its National Museum of the American Indian—has a collection of his material goods which represent 25 plant species and one lichen once used by the Arikara people. These are noted in the plant list below. And although the largest amount of unpublished material was Arikara, there was unique ethnobotanical information found on the following tribes: Dakota, Lakota, Omaha, Onondaga, Oneida, Osage, Pawnee, Potawatomi, Seneca, and Winnebago. Ideally, the cultural information and traditional ecological knowledge contained in these lists will be repatriated with the help of tribal collaborators.

9. Updating and Supplementing the Arikara Language Data

Once Gilmore's ethnographic materials had been organized into the present manuscript, his original Arikara transcriptions were updated to the modern orthography (see Pronunciation Guide for details). Sutton compared Gilmore's written forms of Arikara names to terms in the Arikara Dictionary Database, based on the extensive language documentation work of Douglas Parks. Most of the terms had been recorded from Parks' Arikara consultants in the late twentieth century and could be directly re-transcribed using modern conventions. Of those that had not been so recorded, all but a couple could be interpreted with reasonable certainty. This was possible due both to the structure of Arikara words—where the majority of vocabulary consists of compounds and derivations on the basis of other words—and to comparison with cognate terms in the closely related Pawnee language. The composition of each Arikara name, where applicable, is provided with each plant description.

On the basis of the Parks Arikara Dictionary Database, and more directly on his original notebooks (Parks 1970–1997), we were able to expand the ethnographic description of a number of species, fill in the Arikara terminology that had not been recorded by Gilmore, and fill out the list with even more species. In some cases these additions verify important uses. In other cases, the traditional Arikara usage of these additional plants may not have been documented, but these additions make this list the most comprehensive compendium of Arikara botanical terms currently possible. Citations from Parks' notes are credited to the Arikara speaker who contributed the information and the year recorded in the notebook, but reflect the written representation of the data in the notes and are not necessarily direct quotes of the Arikara consultants themselves.

In addition to updating the scientific and Arikara nomenclature and describing the traditional usage of the plants, several of the descriptions have been enriched with narrative anecdotes. Parks (1991a) contains 156 narratives texts recorded in Arikara, accompanied by English translations (1991b). Within these mythological and historical accounts, the use and significance of many plants is illustrated, whether by explicit comment, whimsical interactions—as in Coyote stories—or offhand inclusion as a part of the traditional daily or seasonal Arikara life. These narratives were culled of all plants mentioned in the list below and summaries of how the plants feature in the stories are included below when appropriate. Such anecdotes further help to capture an original Arikara perspective and voice on these various botanical species.

Additional Ethnobotanical Notes from Historical Travelers

Further comments on traditional botanical use among the Arikara may be drawn from the journals of those who traveled in the early nineteenth century up the Missouri River to the Arikara villages in northern South Dakota. Such historical accounts begin with Meriwether Lewis and William Clark and their famous expedition up the Missouri River in 1804. This visit opened the route for other European-heritage travelers to visit the Arikara and their villages, including Pierre Tabeau, who wrote the *Narrative of the Loisel's Expedition* (Abel 1939), Henry Brackenridge, who accompanied Manual Lisa and his Missouri Fur Company's expedition which traveled up the Missouri River from St. Louis, and Scottish botanist John Bradbury, who was another member of this latter expedition. On June 14, 1811, Bracken-ridge reported from an Arikara village in northern South Dakota:

> In one of the lodges which we visited, we found the doctor, who was preparing some medicine for a sick lad. He was cooling with a spoon a decoction of some roots, which had a strong taste and smell, not unlike jalap [a purgative drug derived from the tubers of a Mexican climbing plant; Kindscher notes that the Arikara medicine most likely included *Echinacea angustifolia*]. He showed us a variety of samples which he used. The most of them were common plants with some medicinal properties, but rather harmless than otherwise. The boy had a slight pleurisy. The chief remedy for their diseases, which they contrive to be owing to a disorder of the bowels, is rubbing the belley [sic] and sides of the patient, sometimes with such violence, as to cause fainting. When they become dangerous, they resort to charms and incantations, such as singing, dancing, blowing on the sick, & etc. They are very successful in the treatment of wounds. When the wound becomes very obstinate, they commonly burn it, after which it heals more easily (Brackenridge 1814).

10. Discussion of Arikara Plant Uses

Once the Arikara Ethnobotany database was complete, the 1050 specific entries from Gilmore were sorted according to both tribal and scientific species names to begin the writing process, and the copied material was referenced for details. Of the total of 106 species (103 plant species) used by the Arikara tribe (see Appendix 1), the largest use was for medicinal purposes (42 species), followed by food (27 species), manufacture (25 species), craft (10 species), perfume (6 species), incense (4 species), horse food (5 species), hunting (4 species), smoking (4 species), and dye plants (3 species), with some of these uses overlapping.

Arikara people certainly used more native species than listed here; based on some of our other work (Kindscher 1987, 1992), we would estimate that likely 200–300 or more species were traditionally used. Gilmore and others had relatively limited interview time with a relatively limited number of people in a postcolonial cultural situation. This surely limited the number of plants recorded. In addition, not all plants used are common, many are difficult to find, or only available during a narrow time window. And some are not located near to the traditional Arikara earth lodge villages or to their contemporary reservation homes. These included: *Actaea rubra* and *Sanginaria canadensis*, likely collected in Minnesota; *Cucurbita foetidissima* coming from southern Nebraska or further south; *Lomatium dissectum* coming from Montana; and *Picea glauca* coming from NW South Dakota, the Black Hills of South Dakota, or Montana. Not surprisingly, the range of plant use was large, and substantial travel could have been involved to obtain a specimen. Even if some of these plants were traded from other tribes, it shows the impressive geographic range of plant knowledge.

Also, of the 103 plant taxa that we compiled the following genera have more than one species in present-day North Dakota which would have likely been used: *Alliuim, Amaranthus, Astragalus, Chenopodium, Cirsium, Crataegus, Equisetum, Liatris, Mentzelia, Opuntia, Physalis, Polygonum, Ribes, Rosa, Rubus, Thalictrum,* and *Typha.* For example, many *Amaranthus* species are used for greens, although only one is listed here, and any blackberries (*Rubus* species) that would have been found would have been eaten. Also, as mentioned in the introduction, a traditional Arikara diet was very healthful, high in consumption of greens and plants high in fiber, such as *Amaranthus, Atriplex,* and *Chenopodium,* and many fruits. Such instances of several species of a given genus being used would also have increased the total species count listed above. Finally, the interviews by Gilmore and Parks did not include non-native species, of which many were certainly also used after European colonization. The cultivated plants of the Arikara, with the exception of tobacco (which is included as a medicinal plant), are not included in the current work. Although this ethnobotany is not complete, especially in the plants used for medicine, the wide range of native plants used to improve health is impressive and gives important insights into traditional medical knowledge and practice.

Section 2.

1. The Plant List

**Gilmore (1932) original title: "Some Aboriginal Uses of Plants by the Arikara Indians"
(note: Gilmore original materials below are quoted or followed with a (G)).**

Gilmore opens his original manuscript with an eloquent statement of the ethnobotanical perspective:

> It is always a matter of much interest to observe the relation of a people to the floral environment which surrounds them. Their familiarity, or their lack of acquaintance, with the indigenous flora of the region, and the degree to which they have discovered economic uses for the native plants is an index in some measure of the length of time the given region has been occupied by this people. The manner of life of any primitive people is strongly influenced by their physical environment. Two very important elements of this environment are the native fauna and flora.

> A people restricted to local resources through lack of facilities of transportation for distant products will sometimes show wonderful ingenuity in the utilization of such things as nature has provided for them near at hand. Even a plant which to people of our present form of civilization may seem to be of no significance may be of considerable importance in the economy of a people living under another complex of circumstances. For example, the common cattail of our marshes. In aboriginal times in America this humble plant found many uses for utility and for play among the people of various Indian tribes. It supplied materials for food, for leather dressing, for cushions, for sanitary appliance, and for children's games.

> The Arikaras are a people who, for several centuries, have resided in the Missouri River Valley and the High Plains adjacent thereto, gradually advancing, during that stretch of time, up the course of this river. Gradually they have adjusted themselves to the new floral conditions successively met in the consecutive stages of their northward progress from their former southern habitat. In the following pages I shall discuss some of the uses of the native plants of this region as I have learned them from the Arikara by observation and inquiry during several years, and discuss the uses by that tribe.

The list of Arikara plants below are arranged alphabetically by current scientific name as listed in the USDA Plants Database (USDA, NRCS 2019). If Gilmore had a different scientific name, it is listed next, followed by Gilmore's common name, and a second common name if the USDA Plants Database prefers another name, and the Arikara name and its translation. All Arikara names for plants have been reviewed and updated to the modern standard orthography, with Gilmore's original transcriptions presented in square brackets, where this is informative. Also, Gilmore's specific writings from his original paper comprise about half of the content below. His original text, and text from other papers are in quotes below.

Acer negundo L.

- **Boxelder**
- *uuxaáku'*, in reference to the tree.
- *neesítš* literally (lit. hereafter in text) "knife", in reference to the fruit.

Figure 3. Boxelder, *Acer negundo,* leaves and fruits. Two fruits are joined together by their base, the "handle" of what would appear to be a large-bladed hunting knife as the one in the Arikara story. Photograph by Craig Freeman. Used with permission.

The Arikara name of the tree is *uuxaáku'*, which appears to be an old compound meaning "hair wood": *uúx-u'* "hair" + *haak-* "wood". The name of the seed capsule, *neesítš*, means "knife" because of its resemblance in shape to that of a hunting knife. A charming and fanciful story for small boys was told among the Arikara and repeated by the elder, Albert Simpson (who later became the Arikara tribal chairman) to Gilmore (1927b).

> A story was told to young boys, ten years old or so, to stir their imagination.

> The story, an imaginative one, is that a man was trapping eagles when he heard a voice like a human being, crying and calling *Heeru' neesítš* 'I wish, knife.' He peered out from his concealment, but to his surprise he saw no person, but he saw a coyote trotting along in the coulee. It was the coyote which was crying for a knife. He then heard a voice responding, saying *šíša' šuúhuni'* 'Come here!'

> He saw the coyote go to the place from which came the voice. At that place was a box elder tree. It was the tree which had called the coyote, and it now said, 'Take one of these my seeds, which you see resembling a knife, and strike it on the ground. When you do so it will become a real knife.' The coyote did so, and carried the knife along. Presently he saw a badger, ambling up the hill. He pursued and with his new knife he cut the badger's throat and it bled to death. Then he looked about for his knife, but he found there only the boxelder seed as it was at first (Gilmore 1927b).

Another version of the story, recorded by Gilmore in his field notes was also told by the elder, Crow Ghost in August 1926:

> The story is that long ago a man of the Arikara was holding a fast in a lonely place in the wilderness for four days. At the end of this time he was returning and lay down in the shadow of a tree to rest. He fell asleep. In his sleep he heard someone speaking to him. He awoke and looked about him but saw no man. It seemed it was the boxelder tree which had spoken to him, wishing to show him favor. It said, 'You will observe the shape of my seeds like a knife. Hereafter, when you go to hunt, carry with you a bunch of these seeds and you will have good fortune in the hunt. You will have plenty of game to your knife.'

Boxelder wood also had uses.

> The Arikaras and other tribes on the Missouri River preferred a forked branch of boxelder for making the handle of a bone hoe. The shoulder blade of a buffalo was used for the hoe blade. The handle was of a boxelder branch.

The wood is tough and suited to the purpose, and the angle of branching is just right for the set of the blade (G).

Also, the light-colored inner bark of boxelder was used in making baskets. The light-colored bark contrasts with the red and black inner barks strips in the artistic basketry designs (Gilmore 1925b). There is more discussion of basket making under *Salix amygdaloides*.

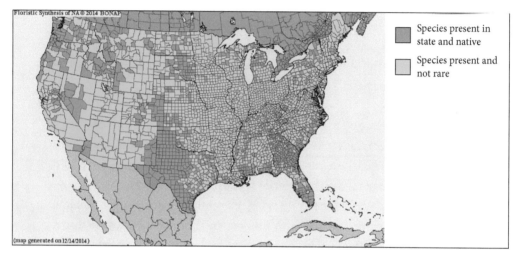

Figure 4. Map of U.S. counties with *Acer negundo* collections.

Figure 5. A traditional burden basket with burden strap/tumpline made by SteštAhkáta of boxelder (the white splints) and red-brown splints, which are made of the dried inner bark of peachleaf willow (*Salix amygdaloides*), to make the artistic pattern. These baskets were used for carrying ears of corn, or harvested plums or chokecherries, to the village. National Museum of the American Indian, Smithsonian Institution, Catalog Number 12/2956.

Achillea millefolium L.

- **Common yarrow, Indian perfume**
- *sakúxtš*

Figure 6. Two white flower tops of common yarrow, *Achillea millefolium,* in a prairie. These plants were important for their scent and medicinal properties. Photograph by Craig Freeman. Used with permission.

According to Ella Waters (Parks 1970–1997): "when the leaf and buds of the plant are crushed in the mouth, they emit a strong odor" (recorded [rec. hereafter in text] 1976). "It was used together with Red baneberry (*škanikaátit*; *Actaea rubra*) for eye medicine when one had sore eyes. The top of the plant was dampened, then rubbed on the hair and the dance outfit" (rec. ca. 1979).

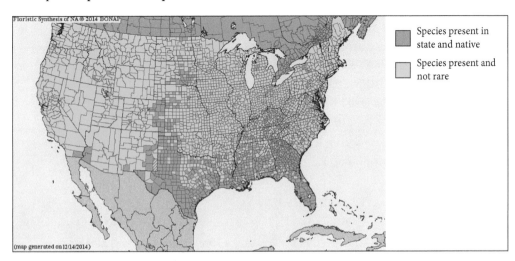

Figure 7. Map of U.S. counties with *Achillea millefolium* collections.

Acorus americanus (Raf.) Raf.

- called *A. calamus* by Gilmore
- **Calamus** or **Sweetflag**
- *kAséhtš*

Figure 8. Plants of calamus or sweetflag, *Acorus americanus,* growing in the Pharmacy Garden at the University of Kansas. The rhizomes were an important Arikara medicine. Photograph by Kelly Kindscher.

The Arikara name *kAséhtš* appears to be a derivation meaning "little root/herb in the water": *kas-* "root, herb" + **ha'iit* "in water" + *-tš* "diminutive suffix".

> Calamus was very highly valued for many medicinal uses. It is said to be good for toothache by chewing some of the rhizome and holding it against the affected tooth.

> When on a hazardous undertaking, it is believed to be a good thing to have some of the rhizome of calamus in the mouth. Then no harm can overtake one. It is also believed if one goes where there is danger from rattlesnakes, a bit of calamus held in the mouth will prevent the person from being bitten by the rattlesnakes. It is especially useful to ward off the 'dangers of the night' such as evil powers and ghosts (G).

According to Ella Waters (Parks 1970–1997),

> it was also said to be effective for treating a sore throat, and was also used to protect oneself from the "bad medicine" of other people. Also, the roots

of sweetflag were broken up and parched, then mixed with other roots and ground up. The resulting powder was put into the mouth of a horse to revive it when it was tired (rec. ca. 1979).

Gilmore also wrote:

This plant is highly valued by Indians of all tribes. Each place where it is found in the Great Plains is well known to all the tribes far around. There is a marshy place in the Mouse River valley west of Towner, North Dakota in which there is a considerable tract of calamus growing. This tract is well known to surrounding tribes. It appears probable that long ago Indian priests and doctors purposely introduced and set the plant in the localities in the Great Plains where it is now found so far from its range (Gilmore 1921).

Also,

the Arikara, and Indians of other tribes as well, are always very greatly pleased to receive presents of rhizomes of calamus. This plant is not found in the Arikara country. At one time, when I brought a present of some calamus to an Arikara, he received it with expressions of great thankfulness and took the rhizomes into his hands in a reverent manner and blessed himself by the usual gestures of blessing, stroking first his right hand reverently over the plant and passing it then over his head, shoulders and body, and then repeated the gesture with his left hand in a similar manner (G).

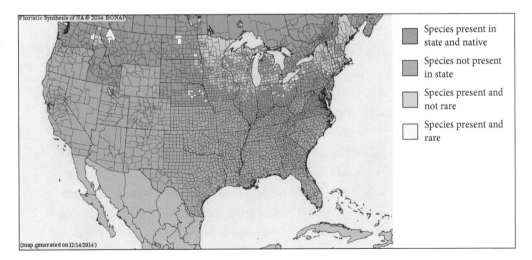

Figure 9. Map of U.S. counties with *Acorus americanus* collections.

Actaea rubra (Aiton) Willd.

- called *A. arguta* by Gilmore
- **Red baneberry**
- *škanikaátit*, lit. "dark many hands"
- *škanitaaká*, lit. "white many hands"

Figure 10. Red baneberry, *Actaea rubra,* was considered by the Arikara to be one of their most important medicines, used for colds, headache, and to treat catfish sting wounds. Photograph by Robyn Klein. Used with permission.

The regular Arikara name *škanikaátit* translates to "dark many hands": *iš-uʾ* "hand" + **kani* "many" + *-kaatiit* "dark", in reference to the fine black roots near the surface of the earth. It is based on the same lexical stem as *Thalictrum* "meadow rue" *škanítš* (lit. "little many hands") and thus could also be interpreted to mean "dark meadow rue". A second, similar term was documented for an unidentified plant, *škanitaaká,* meaning literally "white many hands" (or "white meadow rue" or "white *A. rubra*"). This term may just refer to a Red baneberry plant with white berries, which occasionally occur.

> They consider this plant one of their most valued medicines for various ailments. For a cold on the chest the root of this plant was pulverized and mixed with certain other medicinal plants whose identity I have not yet learned, and an infusion was made to be taken internally. As a remedy for headache, the root was infused and both taken internally and applied externally to the head. It is said to give cooling relief.
>
> Another use is related to the Arikara belief or superstition in regard to supposed 'prenatal influence' on an unborn child. This belief is not peculiar to Arikara alone. White people also hold this belief to some extent, that is, that if a mother sees some startling sight during the period of gestation, it will have the effect to put upon the child some birthmark. This is the popular superstition in this regard among White people. But with the Arikara there

is the additional feature in their belief that a startling experience by either mother or father during the period of the mother's pregnancy will cause a 'mark' upon the child. According to Arikara belief, this 'mark' may be either physical or psychical.

My informant (Albert Simpson) told me of such a case in his own family as he thoroughly believed. He said that one of his children, a boy, was ailing during infancy, and they could not tell what the ailment was. He called in a medicine man who examined the child and diagnosed it as a case of 'birthmark'. He said to the father of the child: 'During the time of your wife's pregnancy with this child you were startled by the sight of a snake and that affected the child.' The father then recalled that he had indeed been startled one time during that period by the sight of a snake. So he believed it was true that this fact had had a bad effect upon the unborn child.

Then the medicine man made an infusion of the roots of red baneberry and of certain other medicinal roots. He burned some sweet grass as incense. Then he held up the child by the shoulders and, taking the medicinal infusion into his mouth, he sprayed the child's body with it. It is said the child's suspended body 'wriggled like a snake' and then became quiet and that it afterwards recovered from its ailment and became perfectly well.

In the first bath of a newborn Arikara child, an infusion of the roots of red baneberry was used to wash out the mouth, nostrils and eyes. Then a drop of this infusion mingled with a certain other medicine, (identity unknown to me), was placed in the right side of its mouth if the infant was a girl, and in the left side of the mouth if a boy.

If the mother has not a sufficient flow of milk for her infant, an infusion of the root of red baneberry is used to bathe her breasts. They believed this will cause an increased flow of milk. In case of inflammation of the breasts, some root of red baneberry is pulverized and mixed with the powdery mass of spores of a ripe puffball to make a poultice to apply. It is said this quickly relieves the pain and swelling (G).

In support of Gilmore's observation, Ella Waters affirmed this and stated (Parks 1970–1997):

baneberry was also used with other roots as eye medicine, to remove cataracts (ca. 1972, 1976). Also, the treatment of red or sore eyes was accomplished by a mixture of Common Yarrow (*sakúxtš*) and Red Baneberry (*škanikaátit*). Roots of the latter and leaves of *sakúxtš* were boiled into tea, which was then put into the eyes to reduce inflammation and soreness (ca. 1979).

Gilmore also stated:

> *Actaea rubra* is also the medicine provided for use in case a man is stung by the catfish while he is operating a fish trap. When a man undertakes the setting up and operating of a fish trap there are certain mystical requirements connected therewith. He must make the required sacrifices and offerings and prayers; he must abstain from connection with his wife, and he must purify himself in the vapor bath. And he must approach the undertaking in a proper attitude of mind, having a feeling of reverence for all nature, and of gratitude to the river and to the fish. If he does not so prepare himself, he will be severely punished by the poisonous stinging of the catfish when he enters the trap to lift them out with the dipping basket. As a remedy for the effects of such stinging the chewed root of *Actaea rubra* must be applied and rubbed into the wounds (Gilmore 1924a).

An image of the plant and also Gilmore's multiple photos and a film, now video of the fish trap as used in the Missouri River are in the Smithsonian Institution collections.

Gilmore developed a remarkable trust with SteštAhkáta, (Yellow Corn Woman). She was 86 when he interviewed her in 1926 and willing to share with him detailed information for his paper, "Notes on the Gynecology and Obstetrics of the Arikara" (1931a), and he elsewhere described her as the "most skilled midwife of the Arikara" (Gilmore 1927a). The baneberry was also used related to childbirth and according to SteštAhkáta:

> When delivery seems to be unduly delayed, some of the medicine mentioned before is put upon the top of the woman's head. This medicine is an infusion of the roots of the red baneberry (*Actaea rubra*). The midwife also takes some of the medicine into her mouth and sends it forcibly into the mouth of the woman. It is supposed that this will 'scare the baby,' so that it will quickly move down and be delivered. At the same time the midwife takes in hand a wisp of wild sage (*Artemisia ludoviciana*) which she has ready. With it she brushes downward on the woman's body in front, both right and left sides, and then down the back, with four sweeping motions from head to feet. It is said that when all this is done, the delivery is no longer delayed, and the baby comes quickly.

In case of postpartum hemorrhage the juice of the chokecherry is given to the patient to drink. Also in such cases the gum which exudes from the *nakaaNUstaáku'* 'chokecherry tree' (*Prunus virginiana*) is triturated [finely ground] together with the root of *paatAhuunuukaásu'* 'scarlet globemallow' (*Sphaeralcea coccinea*) and made into an infusion which is given as a drink (Gilmore 1931a).

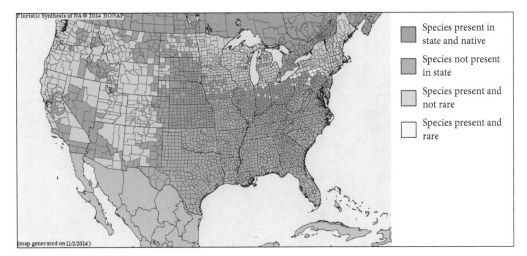

Figure 11. Map of U.S. counties with *Actaea rubra* collections.

Figure 12. A fish trap made by White Bear (*KuuNUxtaaká*) required many specific plant species for its making. In addition, catching catfish always poses the risk of being stung by their venomous spines of the dorsal and pectoral fins. Therefore when make a trap, a root of red baneberry must be on hand as it, and sandbar willow (*Salix interior*) bark, are applied and rubbed into any catfish "stinging". The photograph was by Melvin Gilmore, at the edge of the Missouri River on the Fort Berthold Reservation in 1923. Catfish were regularly caught and shared when the fish trap was used. National Museum of the American Indian, Smithsonian Institution, Catalog Number NO8716.

Agastache foeniculum (Pursh) Ktze.

- **Wild anise** or **Blue giant hyssop**
- *kAhahtAtwaarúxti'*
- *sčireéšu'*

Figure 13. Wild anise, *Agastache foeniculum,* was used to perfume valuable items and was made into a beverage tea. Photograph by Robyn Klein. Used with permission.

The Arikara name for this plant means "holy fragrant plant": *kahaan-* "odor, smell" + *taát-u'* "stem, plant" + *waaruxtii* "holy". Gilmore explains that "[t]he Arikara name of this plant, *kahts-waruhti,* or *kat'tu-waruhti* 'holy medicine,' [derives] from *kahtsu,* 'medicine,' and *waruhti,* 'holy'" (G). See also the entry for *Monarda fistulosa,* where he also used the transcription *kat'tu.* He may have mistaken the *kAhahtAt-* "fragrant plant" part in these entries for *kás-u'* "herb, root". Wild anise was also recorded as *sčireéšu'* from some Arikara speakers, a word which otherwise refers to Wild mint (Parks 1970–1997).

"The leaves and tops of this plant were used for perfuming clothing, blankets, etc., being put away with clothing as lavender is by White people." Angela Plante separately affirmed this use (Parks 1970–1997) and also clarified that the dried leaves and tops were used for this purpose (rec. 1996). Gilmore also stated that wild anise

> was used by men to perfume their eagle wing fans, their clothing and etc. In addition, it was used also to make a tea-like drink, being steeped in hot water. It was regarded as a pleasant, cooling drink for hot weather. The infusion of its leaves was also taken as a remedy for fever as a carminative [to relieve gas], especially for infants. The leaves were also used to rub on the body in the bath lodge for their cooling effect after the hot vapor bath (G).

Leaves and tips of this plant collected and annotated by Gilmore are in the Smithsonian Institution collections, NMAI #122986.

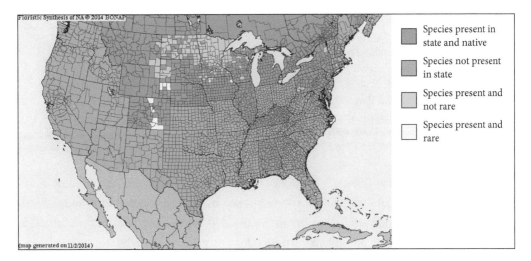

Figure 14. Map of U.S. counties with *Agastache foeniculum* collections.

Allium spp.

- **Onion**
- *koóxu'*

Figure 15. Round umbel inflorescence of a wild onion, *Allium canadense,* which were used by the Arikara as food, usually cooked because they were recognized to cause bad breath. Photograph by Craig Freeman. Used with permission.

According to Ella Waters (Parks 1970–1997), this name was used for both wild onions and the commercial onion of today. Onions were cooked by boiling in water, maybe thickened slightly, then consumed in soup. Raw onions were eaten by children, but not by adults, who wanted them cooked. Raw onion had a strong odor and gave bad breath (rec. 1972).

Figure 16. Map of U.S. counties with *Allium* species collections.

Amaranthus spp.

- **Amaranth** or **Pigweed**
- *pís*

Figure 17. Lush, densely vegetated row of amaranth (*Amaranthus tuberculatus*) being grown for seed, which was used by the Arikara historically as a lure for snaring or hunting birds. Photograph by Kelly Kindscher.

"Seeds used as lure for birds. Flocking birds snared or shot with blunt arrows" (G).

The Arikara name appears to be homophonous with the word *pís* meaning "lice", which also appears in several compound words suggesting tiny objects (as well as in words suggesting filth). The name of *Amaranthus* may thus be a reference to the small seeds. Or, it could simply be an unrelated homophonous word.

Figure 18. Map of U.S. counties with *Amaranthus* species collections.

Amelanchier alnifolia (Nutt.) Nutt. ex M. Roem

- **Juneberry** or **Saskatoon serviceberry**
- *naakunaánu'*, in generic reference to the berry
- *naakuNAhtaátu'*, in specific reference to the bush
- Apparently means "earth wood": *rak-* "wood" + *hunaán-u'* "earth" (+ *taát-u'* "stem, plant").

Figure 19. The attractive white flowers of juneberry, *Amelanchier alnifolia,* are followed by tasty purple fruits, that were an important Arikara fruit, including one of their favorite traditional flavorings of cornballs. Photograph by Craig Freeman. Used with permission.

As Gilmore documented in his publication, titled "Arikara Commerce", according to SteštAhkáta, in the olden days, in their trade with the Lakota the serviceberry or juneberry was the same price as chokecherries: although serviceberries were easier to prepare for drying than chokecherries, "they were harder to gather" (Gilmore 1926a).

In an unpublished recipe for cornballs (*štípii'It*), Ella P. Waters mentions *naakunaánu'* as one potential additive for flavoring (Parks 1970–1997).

That juneberries were sometimes considered a favored snack can be gleaned from a story told by Alfred Morsette (Parks 1991a:216–239). In this story, a man with powers would end up killing any suitors who attempted to court his beautiful daughter: he would demand the men perform impossible tasks and murder them when they failed. One of the tasks set before the suitor protagonist of the story is to retrieve *naakunaánu'* for the man in the middle of winter, when no berries are normally found. Fortunately the young man is pitied by *SkuuNUxwáhAt* Red Bear Woman, one of the beings who had granted the evil man his powers and are upset about the abuse. The young man takes a branch of the *naakuNAhtaátu'*, climbs up to the smokehole of Red Bear Woman's earthlodge and shakes the branch. The branch magically becomes loaded with berries and the boy takes it back to his evil father-in-law, accomplishing the impossible task.

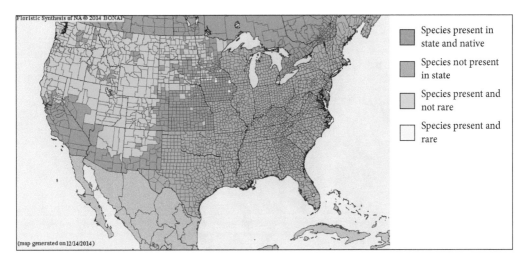

Figure 20. Map of U.S. counties with *Amelanchier alnifolia* collections.

Figure 21. A berry box/container would be used for gathering or storing juneberries and other fruits. This "berry bag" was made from hide and collected from Cedar Woman by Melvin Gilmore in 1923. National Museum of the American Indian, Smithsonian Institution, Catalog Number 12/2968.

Amorpha fruticosa L.

- **Indigo bush** or **false indigo bush**
- *čiiraáxu'*, lit. "lightning streak"

Figure 22. Indigo bush, *Amorpha fruticosa,* had many uses, including the stems being used as arrow shafts and the foliage being used as a ceremonial incense. Photograph by Michael Haddock. Used with permission.

The shrub usually forms straight, even stems of light weight. They are therefore useful to make arrow-shafts by the Arikara. Dried stems of this shrub were employed to ignite at the fireplace in the sacred lodge (tribal temple) and carry a light to light the sacred pipe in the ceremonies.

Amorpha fruticosa is used as an incense in the ritual pertaining to Thunder, a ritual to avert lightning strike or to make propitiation for any offense which may draw punishment by lightning. When lightning strikes near a man's house, it is a warning that he has offended some Higher Power, either by omission or commission. He may have committed some positive offense, wittingly or unwittingly, or he may have neglected, when he obtained game in the hunt, to make an offering of a small morsel of the meat as an acknowledgement for the favor, or to apologize should he have neglected some other duty to the supernatural powers.

One must not go near a place where lightning has struck until four days have passed unless a man who has the Thunder (Lightning) ritual, makes a ceremony at the place, using the fruits of this *Amorpha* as an incense (G).

This association with lightning undoubtedly is the source of the Arikara name for the plant.

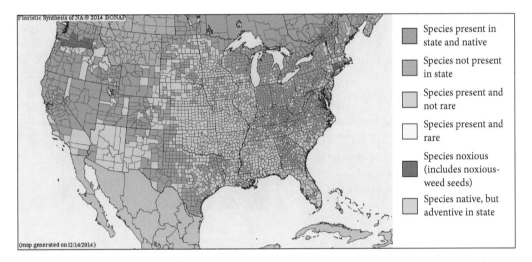

Figure 23. Map of U.S. counties with *Amorpha fruticosa* collections.

Amorpha nana Nutt.

- called *A. microphylla* by Gilmore
- **Least amorpha** or **dwarf false indigo**
- *huhčipáts̆, čipáts̆*

Figure 24. The powdered root of dwarf false indigo, *Amorpha nana,* was used as a medicine to stop bleeding. Photograph by Craig Freeman. Used with permission.

The Arikara name is a compound of *huún-u'* "grass" and *čipáts̆* "knotweed", although Gilmore also records it being called simply *čipáts̆*.

> The leaves of this tiny shrub were used by women for decorative patterns for porcupine quill embroidery, and especially on the head chief's tunic. The roots of the shrub were used medicinally as a styptic [to stop bleeding]. For this purpose, they were pounded in a mortar until finely pulverized. For use, a sufficient quantity of this powder was placed in a medicine bowl made of ash wood. Hot water was poured into the bowl and the powder was stirred as it steeped. The water turned red. In case of nasal hemorrhage this was snuffed up the nostrils. The dry powder might also be snuffed into the nostrils for nasal hemorrhage, and with like effect, but perhaps with less prompt action. The powder was also applied as a styptic in case of a severed vein or artery (G).

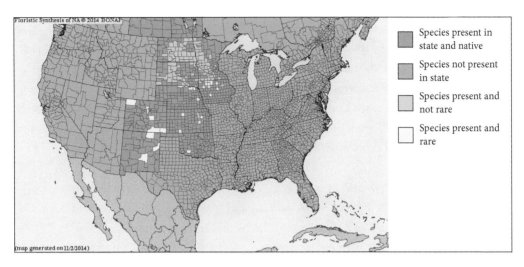

Figure 25. Map of U.S. counties with *Amorpha nana* collections.

Amphicarpaea bracteata (L.) Fernald

- **Ground bean** or **American hogpeanut**
- *atikAhunaánu'*, lit. "wild bean"

Figure 26. The distinctive three leaflets of the ground bean, *Amphicarpaea bracteata,* produced flowers, followed by seeds and fruits that were used as food, and stories were told of the fruits also being gathered from bean mice caches. Photograph by Craig Freeman. Used with permission.

The Arikara name, meaning "wild bean" is a compound of *átit* "bean" + *kAhunaán-u'* "wilderness".

The Arikara use of the American hog peanut, which Gilmore called the "bean", was introduced to the Lewis and Clark Expedition when the expedition met the Arikara, near present-day Cannonball, North Dakota. William Clark on October 11, 1804 described that they ate "a large well flavoured Been which they rob the Mice of in the Plains and is verry nurishing" (Lewis et al. 2002). Gilmore has written the story of the ground bean and its food use by many central Plains tribes and how the Missouri River bean mouse (*Microtus pennsylvanicus*) collects the beans (also see Bailey 1920).

> The beans are like peanuts in that they flower above ground, but then some flowers bury themselves in the ground and make larger soft beans, which the mice gather. The Arikara people knew this and would trade, or leave as an offering for the mice, some corn or suet or other food in exchange for the beans that they would take from their stores. There was much respect for the bean mouse as an industrious being, who even helps people (Gilmore 1925a).

In Matthew White Bear's story of Bear Man (Parks 1991a:1197–1211), Bear Man's mother is abducted and impregnated by a mythical bear while she and her sister are out gathering *atikAhunaánu'*. The story follows the adventures of her son after he kills the bear, as he becomes chief of an Arikara village. The story opens with a group of young women exclaiming, *toosuxtahná'At atikAhunaánu'!* "Let's go gather ground beans!" Bear Man's mother is abducted into the bear's den when she and a friend separate to pick the prolific beans growing around a large rock. This is a common scene-setting device in Arikara stories, dramatic occurrences following as a woman would go out into the wilderness to gather wild plants. Such stories may have helped to reinforce wariness of dangers when leaving the village.

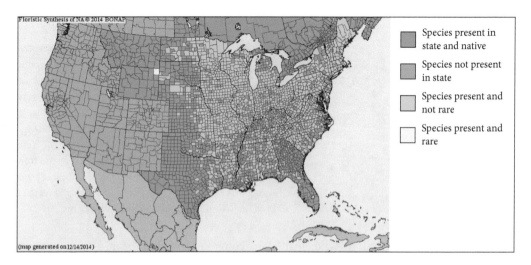

Figure 27. Map of U.S. counties with *Amphicarpaea bracteata* collections.

Andropogon gerardii Vitman

- called *A. furcatus* by Gilmore
- **Bluestem grass** or **Big bluestem**
- *huhwáhAt, huhpáhAt, haaNUtwáhAt*, lit. "red grass"

Figure 28. A waving prairie field of big bluestem or turkey foot bluestem (*Andropogon gerardii*), with inflorescences trailing in the wind. The long stems and leaves of this grass were used as thatching, covered by soil, in the roof construction of earth lodges. They were also used to line cache pits where corn and other crops were stored for months at a time. Photograph by Kelly Kindscher.

The names *huhwáhAt* and *huhpáhAt* both signify 'red grass,' *huún-u'*, 'grass' + *-wahat ~ -pahat* 'red.' The same meaning applies to *haaNUtwáhAt*, although this term is based on *haanuút-u'* 'Native dry grass.' These names derive "from the natural coloration which this grass takes on when mature in the fall (G).

This species of grass was used in house-building when mature and dry, being laid on the willow mattress of the roof and then over the grass, earth was laid to a depth of about one foot or more, in the circular wall and the dome-shaped roof of the earth-covered house (Gilmore 1931b).

It was also used for lining storage pits which were excavated underground for storing the crops of corn, beans and other produce and all kinds of food supplies. For this purpose this species of grass was used because it was found, by experience, that it would not mold and decay as other species of grass did when in contact with the earth.

Temporary ropes were made by twisting together to any length required, the soft basal blades of this grass (G).

A few turns would be taken in twisting, then the rope pulled to loosen a little more material, then a few more twists taken, and so on till as much rope was made as required.

For belated planting of both corn and squashes, the seeds were placed in a bed of the soft lower blades of bluestem grass, dampened, wrapped in a piece of rawhide, and suspended above the fireplace.

In making arrows of the stems of this wild grass small, boys of the Arikara, Mandan, and Hidatsa tribes would commonly insert a thorn of *Crataegus* sp. (thorn apple) for an arrow point. With such arrows to their little bows they would train themselves to skill in archery by shooting frogs (Gilmore 1977).

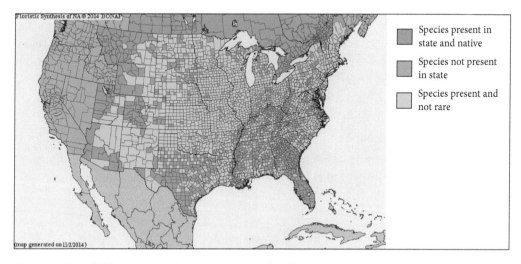

Figure 29. Map of U.S. counties with *Andropogon gerardii* collections.

Anemone cylindrica Gray

- **Cylindric anemone, Thimbleweed**
- *kAskAhúhtu'*, lit. "down-feather weed"
- *kAhúhtu' taátu'*, lit. "down-feather plant"
- *taátu' saakAxtItkú'u'*, lit. "mouse tail plant"

Figure 30. The white fluff of thimbleweed, *Anemone cylindrical,* was used as absorbent padding inside soft buckskin, in the care of infants, instead of to-day's diapers. Photograph by Katy Chayka. Used with permission.

The Arikara name, *kAskAhúhtu'* … [is] compounded from *kás-u'*, 'herb or root (in reference to a small and useful plant)', and *kAhúht-u'* 'down-feather'. Thus the name *kAskAhúhtu'* is descriptive, referring to the feathery appearance of the seed-head of the plant when the seed begins to shed. Gilmore's recorded alternative name *kAhúhtu' taátu'* simply swaps out *kás-u'* 'herb, root' for *taát-u'* 'plant, stem', while the name *taátu' saakAxtItkú'u'* (*saákAx* 'mouse' + *NItkú-u'* 'tail') appears to describe the long, narrow stem itself.

According to Albert Simpson, in the old times, the down of this plant was also used for absorbent padding in the care of infants, just as cat-tail down was used, and was preferred for very young infants because it is softer. A breechcloth of soft buckskin was used for this purpose, and the down was packed inside.

The root of this plant had some medicinal use according to Albert Simpson [interviewed on August 24 and 25, 1926], but what it was I have not yet learned (G).

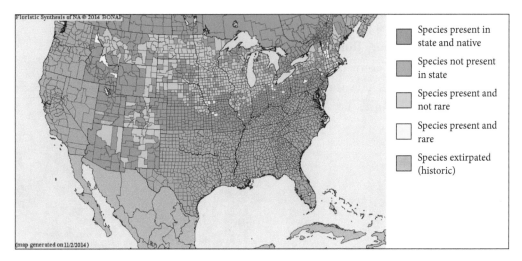

Figure 31. Map of U.S. counties with *Anemone cylindrica* collections.

Anemone virginiana L.

- **Anemone** or **Tall thimbleweed**
- *naaWIhkahUhnaaNIsawaáhUx*, lit. "weed with cotton hanging on"

Figure 32. The capsules of the tall thimbleweed, *Anemone virginiana*, would ripen and the fluff was also be used as absorbent padding in the care of infants. Photograph by Michael Haddock. Used with permission.

The Arikara name is comprised of: *naaWIhkAhúht-u'* "cotton" (lit. "down feather cloth") + *ran-* "plural" + *-isawaa* "be hanging" + *-hUx* "-er".

Note that Gilmore's analysis appears to be largely accurate, if mis-segmented: "The name *Nakaȟnansawauȟ* ('weed with cotton hanging on'), *nakaȟ*, 'cotton,' *nansa*, 'hanging on,' and *wahu*, 'planting.'" This word was not verified with a fluent speaker using modern linguistic methods, thus the modern transcription is based entirely on Gilmore's information. In this regard, Gilmore's transcription of the part meaning "cotton", *nakaȟ*, is a particularly poor representation of *naaWIhkahUh-*, the Arikara root for "cotton" as it would appear in this word form. This discrepancy introduces some doubt in the updated transcription.

"The cottony seed of this plant was used in sanitary care of the new-born babies" (G).

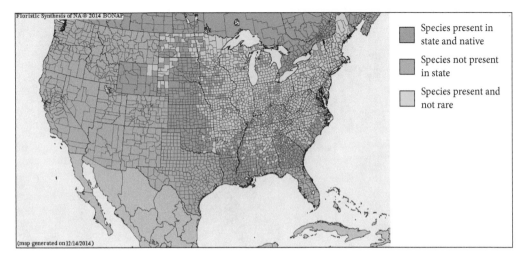

Figure 33. Map of U.S. counties with *Anemone virginiana* collections.

Apocynum cannabinum L.

- **Dogbane, Indian hemp**
- *šwaahIhníkUx, šwaahiíkUx, šwaahií'It*, lit. "hand burner"
- *naaWIhkAhuNAhtaátu'*, lit. "cotton stem"

Figure 34. Bright green leaves of dogbane (*Apocynum cannabinum*) with distinct red stems and cream-colored inflorescences. Mature stem fibers were used for cordage and the roots were used for an Arikara medicine. Photograph by Craig Freeman. Used with permission.

The primary Arikara name means "hand burner": *íš-u'* "hand" + *-waahihnik* "burn (transitive)" + *-hUx* "-er". This analysis reflects the name as given by Gilmore (and the first of the modern transcriptions) and reflects the irritating properties of the milky sap. The other two variants of the name were recorded by Douglas Parks in the late twentiety century and are based on the stem *-waahik* "burn (intransitive)" (Parks 1970–1997). Another name noted in connection with *Apocynum* by Gilmore, *naaWIhkAhuNAhtaátu'*, is composed of *naaWIhkAhúht-u'* "cotton" + *-ran* "PL" + *taát-u'* "stem". This perhaps refers to the silky fibers associated with the seeds looking like cotton or milkweed seed fluff.

> Among all tribes in the range of this plant its fiber was used to twine cordage and thread. Information I had from the Iroquois of New York and from

the Arikara of North Dakota is that the fiber was obtained from the previous year's stalks which had become naturally retted [softened] by standing where they grew and being weathered through all the year (G).

From Gilmore's July 22, 1926 field notes:

I have seen the process of making twine by an old Arikara man named Yellow Bird. The retted stalks were gathered and heckled [to straighten or split the fibers] between his teeth and carded with his fingers, and the fibers twined by rolling under the palm of the hand on the bare leg, and showed himself a master workman of the job. Such rope, twine and string were used for all purposes for which cordage of any kind was required.

The fibers then were spun by twining, rolling the strands on the leg under the palm of the hand. Information I had from the Iroquois is that besides cordage there was also a fabric woven from thread twined from the fibers of this plant. It was woven into a textile band for holding sanitary pads in place. These pads were felted from the fine, soft, silky coma of the ripe seeds of the common wild milkweed, *Asclepias syriaca*. Or sometimes these sanitary pads were made from certain soft lichens.

The roots of the plant were used medicinally. Mixed with some other plant products not yet identified, and finely pulverized, it was presented to the nostrils of a patient in a stupor, and it caused him to rouse (G).

Ella Waters (rec. ca. 1979) commented that

in this form, it could also be used as a sneezing powder and to relieve headaches. Also, it was believed that when a root is dug once, it will not grow in that area again and one would have to look for it elsewhere (Parks 1970–1997).

Šwaahií'It, one variant of the term for Dogbane, is also the name of an evil witch woman in a story told by Alfred Morsette (Parks 1991a:82–90). The character would kill people and turn their flesh into bags (*niikarúxtš*) by blowing into their mouths. She is defeated and killed when the story's protagonist, a boy born from a stone impregnating his mother, throws *Šwaahií'It*'s heart into a fire. It is unclear why the witch is named *Šwaahií'It* and whether it historically has anything to do with Dogbane.

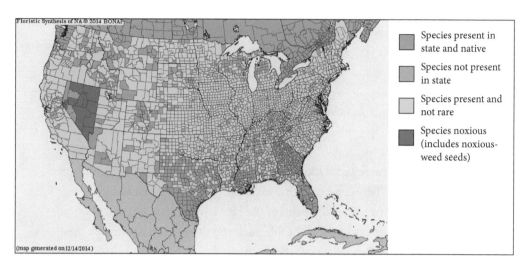

Figure 35. Map of U.S. counties with *Apocynum cannabinum* collections.

Arctostaphylos uva-ursi (L.) Spreng.

- **Kinnikinnick** or **Bearberry**
- *kUxapAhkáxIš, kUxapukáxIš,* lit. "hard sandcherry"

Figure 36. The waxy leaves and unripe green berries of kinnikinnick or bearberry, *Arctostaphylos uva-ursi,* was the important ingredient in the smoking mix, which was also called kinnikinnick. Photograph by Kelly Kindscher.

The Arikara names are two variants of a descriptive compound of *kUxapaán-u'* "sandcherry" (cf. *Prunus pumila* below) + *-kaxiš* "hard, solid, tough". The fruit is on a leafy, woody plant, similar to a sand cherry, but smaller, ground-hugging, and the fruits are harder.

> The dried leaves of this plant were an important part of the smoking mix (*kinnikinnick*), with it and the inner bark of red osier dogwood, (*Cornus sericea*), being added to the leaves of the special tobacco (*Nicotiana quadrivalvis*) that the Arikara cultivated for its use (Gilmore 1926b).

Alfred Morsette (rec. 1979), as well as Lillian Brave and Angela Plante (rec. 1987), reported that

> the plants grow in clumps and are said to be red on one side and green on the other, with elongated oval leaves and three round marble-sized "balls" under the leaves. Also the plants were dipped in boiling kidney fat, then hung up to dry (Parks 1970–1997).

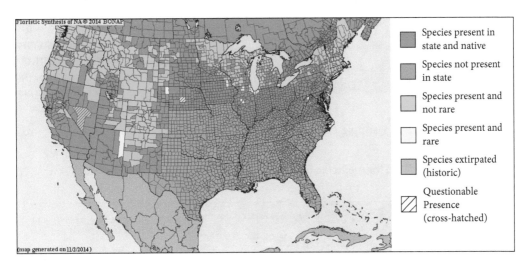

Figure 37. Map of U.S. counties with *Arctostaphylos uva-ursi* collections.

Artemisia dracunculus L.

- **Tarragon** or **Tall green Artemisia, Green Sage**
- *nakáxIš*, lit. "hard wood"
- *čipátš*, lit. "(knot)weed"

Figure 38. This harvested wild tarragon, *Artemisia drancunculus,* with yellow-green blooms contrasting against a limestone slab of rock was traditionally used by the Arikara as part of a medicine to wash sores. Photograph by Kelly Kindscher.

The Arikara name is a simple descriptive compound: *rak- ~ haak-* "wood, tree" + *-kaxiš* "hard, solid".

This plant was "used for medicine mixed with other medicines and used to wash sores" (G).

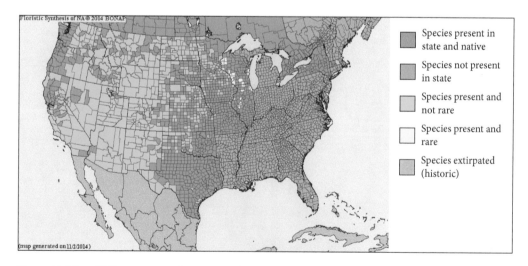

Figure 39. Map of U.S. counties with *Artemisia dracunculus* collections.

Artemisia frigida Willd.

- **Least wild sage** or **Prairie sagewort, fringed sagebrush**
- *čeewa'út*
- *čeewohkooháhkAt,* lit. "Artemisia on the prairie"

Figure 40. Fringed sagebrush, *Artemisia frigida,* has aromatic foliage, which was used to drive away evil spirits. Photograph by Craig Freeman. Used with permission.

The etymology of this word is not transparent, but the second part, **-wa'ut,* appears to be the same stem as appears in *napu'ut, Artemisia longifolia* below. The second name is a compound of the first with *koocháhkAt* "on the prairie".

> This plant is used medicinally and in religious ceremonies. In ceremonies, a bunch of this species is used to represent those who have gone before. For example, Albert Simpson so used a bunch of this species to represent and to honor the memory of Crow Ghost (*KaakaaneekAsaánu'*), Four Rings (*Sčiškoóku' Čiití'Iš*) and others who had been his teachers.

> This species of *Artemisia* is also used as a brush in the sweat lodge to drive away any disease or evil which might be lurking there. This is to avert evil from the person who is taking the treatment of the vapor bath (G).

In narratives, sage would also be laid down on the floor as bedding or as a seat for special guests (cf. several stories in Parks 1991a). The impoverished character Eats Ashes (*Naanuúsu' Tiwaawa'á*), in a story told by Mary Gillette, chews on *čeewa'út* to stave off his hunger (Parks 1991a:1225).

Figure 41. Map of U.S. counties with *Artemisia frigida* collections.

Artemisia longifolia Nutt.

- **Long-leafed wormwood**
- *napaʾút*

Figure 42. The above ground foliage and stems of long-leaved sage, *Artemisia longifolia*, were used as a bedding, for mats. Photograph by Matt Lavin. Used with permission.

The Arikara name appears to be an old compound: *rak- ~ haak-* "wood" + **-waʾut*. As noted in the preceding entry, **-waʾut* is also found in *čeewaʾút Artemisia frigida*, but has no other known meaning.

"In ancient times, this *Artemisia* was used for bedding, like mats. It is still used this way." It was also "used as a bed for sacred objects in ceremonies, in the Sacred Lodge" (G).

Ella Waters reported (rec. 1979), that "the stem of *Artemisia* was scraped and used as a tobacco tamper. Its leaves were also used for medicine" (Parks 1970–1997).

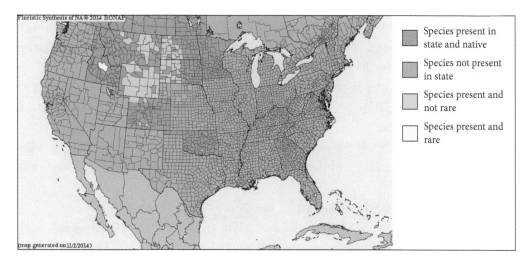

Figure 43. Map of U.S. counties with *Artemisia longifolia* collections.

Artemisia ludoviciana Nutt.

- called *A. gnaphalodes* by Gilmore
- **White sagebrush, White sage, Mugwort** or **Artemisia**
- *čeewohnaaNIšíšu'*

Figure 44. Clusters of white sage (*Artemisia ludoviciana*) and stems were used in sweat lodges for purification, and also used to scrub the body to remove the human scent when trapping eagles or using the fish trap. Photograph by Kelly Kindscher.

"The Arikara name, *čeewohnaaNIšíšu'* means 'the real Artemisia.'" It is comprised of *čeewa'út* "*Artemisia frigida*" (see above) + *naaNIšíš-u'* "real, true, prototypical". It is also called *Čeewostaáka*, literally "white sage": *čeewa'út* "sage" + *taakaan* "white".

"This species is also used medicinally, and also in the vapor bath lodge." Parks (1970–1997) records from an unidentified source that "the top of the plant was rubbed over an ailing area when one had a leg ache."

"It was also used to ward off human scent, as when capturing an eagle" (Gilmore 1929) or when assembling or using a fish trap in the river (Gilmore 1924a). When in an eagle trap,

> you shall have with you in the pit a bundle of artemisia (*Artemisia ludoviciana*). When you have thus settled yourself to watch, you must be quiet but alert. After a while the magpies will discover the bait which you have tied securely with sinew to the frame above your head, and will come and try to take it away. You will remain quiet, not frightening them away. Finally an eagle will observe the magpies and will soar above to investigate. After a while you will notice that the magpies have suddenly flown away. You will know that now the eagle is circling down to the bait. You must now be alert and ready. When he alights you will quickly reach through the framework and seize the eagle by his feet and pull him down into the pit. As you do so you will grasp with your other hand some of the artemisia and thrust if toward the eagle. He will seize the artemisia in his beak and thus you may avoid his snapping and tearing your flesh, and you will grasp and wrench his neck to kill him, being careful to hold firmly the eagle's feet so that he cannot get his talons into your flesh, else he might dangerously lacerate muscles and tendons so that you would be crippled, or he might even tear open an artery so that you would bleed to death (G).

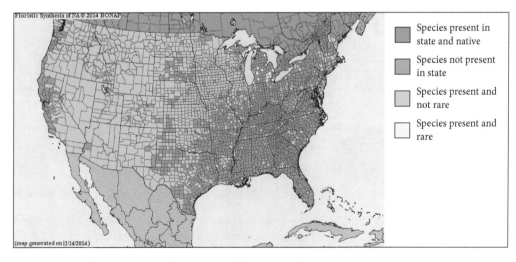

Figure 45. Map of U.S. counties with *Artemisia ludoviciana* collections.

Artemisia tridentata Nutt.

- **Big sagebrush** or **Common sagebrush**
- *napa'út*
- *napohnaáwiš*
- *naakat'ná'*

Figure 46. The sagebrush, *Artemisia tridentata,* had a variety of uses for its wood and also for ceremonial use its fragrant foliage. Photograph by Matt Lavin. Used with permission.

Gilmore lists three names for this plant. The first, *napa'út*, is the same as that given for *Artemisia longifolia* above. The second, *napohnaáwiš*, is descriptive, meaning "gray Artemisia": *napa'út* "Artemisia" + *-raawiš* "smoky, gray". The third name, *naakat'ná'*, undoubtedly reflects its ceremonial usage, meaning "mother wood": *rak-* ~ *haak-* "wood" + *at'ná'* "my/our mother".

> The wood of this shrub has many uses. Among these are the following: for pipe-cleaners, pipe stems, basket-rims, basket handles, frames of baby cradles, decorative rings for bridles, earrings, hobbles for horses, and many other things. When used for hobbles (to keep horses from wandering) they are linked together by thongs. By greasing, heating and straightening it would serve for arrow shafts, when nothing better could be had. Sagebrush branches and wood were also used in ceremonies (G).

Ella Waters commented (rec. ca. 1979) about sagebrush species and varieties: "this is a stiffer, harder kind of *napa'út*. It grows chiefly in Montana and out west. Its stems were also used for pipe tampers. The leaves were also used for medicine" (Parks 1970–1997).

Alfred Morsette, interviewed around the same time (ca. 1979), described yet another variety of *A. tridentata*, which he called *čeewotkaátit, čeewohkaátit* "Black sage", or also *čeewostanáha'*, literally "buffalo sage". These names are based on the *čeewa'út* word seen above for some *Artemisia* species. According to him, it is a type of sage that grows close to the ground and outward, often found around barns, particularly among manure. It is dark in color, leaves over an inch long, dark on top and light on under side, and it smells like Vicks® VapoRub™ (Parks 1970–1997).

Figure 47. Map of U.S. counties with *Artemisia tridentata* collections.

Asclepias syriaca L. and *A. speciosa* Torr.

- **Common milkweed** and **Showy milkweed**
- *sakoxkaá'A*

Figure 48. Beautiful pink flowers of common milk-weed, *Asclepias syriaca*. The buds, young pods, and shoots of the plant were used when tender in the spring, as an important food source. Photograph by Kelly Kindscher.

This is a useful food plant. The young sprouts, the tender young leaves and tips, and the bud clusters and young seed pods were stewed either alone or with green or dried corn or with buffalo meat (G).

Ella Waters (rec. ca. 1979) is a little more specific about the preparation of *Asclepias*: "the flowers and leaves of the milkweed plant were boiled in water, together with a little grease, and then eaten as one eats greens" (Parks 1970–1997).

Gilmore also spoke about common milkweed's medicinal use:

According to the 'doctrine of signatures,' the milky juice of the milkweed was used as a remedy in case a mother had an insufficient flow of milk to suckle her baby. For this purpose the milky juice of the plant was drawn out and mixed in with the strained juice of fresh green corn, or of stewed dried green corn. The woman would drink this mixture. If corn could not be had she would drink the pure juice of the milkweed alone. For four days after childbirth the dose is one half cupful morning and evening. After four days the quantity she may drink is not limited by prescription (G).

In Gilmore's (1926c) article, "Some Interesting Indian Foods", he wrote that:

> common milkweed was also important to making traditional corn bread. Ripe corn was pounded to meal with a pestle in a mortar. The meal was mixed with water and seasoned with salt. The fireplace meantime had been well heated by maintaining a hot fire for a sufficient time. Then the coals and ashes were drawn out, a layer of fresh green leaves of the common big milkweed (*Asclepias syriaca*) was laid in the bottom. The corn meal batter was poured upon this layer of fresh, clean leaves. Then another layer of milkweed leaves was laid over the batter. Then a layer of corn husks was laid over the leaves, then a thick layer of ashes over the corn husks. Last of all a good bed of live coals was laid over the ashes, and the bread was left to bake. The milkweed leaves added moisture and likely flavor to the baking bread.

According to SteštAhkáta, in the cornfields,

> the only weeds which troubled us were milkweed (*Asclepias syriaca*), wild licorice (*Glycyrrhiza lepidota*), lambsquarters (*Chenopodium album*), and tuberous sunflowers, also called 'Jerusalem artichokes,' (*Helianthus tuberosa*). Milkweed and lamb's quarter were not altogether bad for they were good for food, used as greens (Gilmore 1926c).

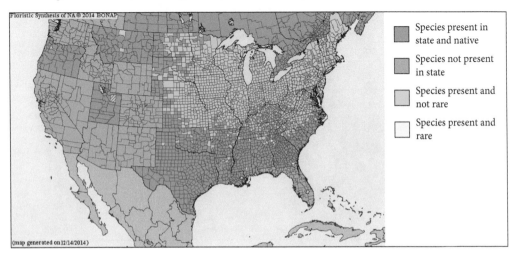

Figure 49. Map of U.S. counties with *Asclepias syriaca* collections.

Astragalus crassicarpus Nutt.

- **Ground plum milkvetch, Buffalo bean/pea**
- *tskAhuunipiíku'*
- *kaanipiíku'*

The first name means literally "egg mash", comprised of *tskahuu* "mashed" + *nipiík-u'* "egg". The second Arikara term—literally "inside egg": *kaa-* "inside" + *nipiík-u'* "egg"—also applies to the cone, bud, or flower of any plant or to a pine cone. The beans of this plant are about the size of a small plum, which grow in clumps close to the ground. According to Ella Waters (rec. ca. 1979), "the bean [actually a fruit, a pod], when dried, was used by children to make strings of beads to wear. They were also strung when green" (Parks 1970–1997).

In addition, two other *Astragalus* species were recorded by John Bradbury as being part of the Arikara medical botany as important medicine in his visit to the Arikara villages in 1811 (Brackenridge 1814). These would be referred to as loco-

Figure 50. The reddish fruits of ground plum milkvetch, *Astragalus crassicarpus,* were dried and strung by children as beads. Photograph by Craig Freeman. Used with permission.

weeds as, unlike ground plum milkvetch, most other *Astragalus* are poisonous due to alkaloids or to accumulation of toxic levels of selenium, or both. Using these poisonous plants as medicine helps demonstrate the Arikara's knowledge and skill at using wild native plants.

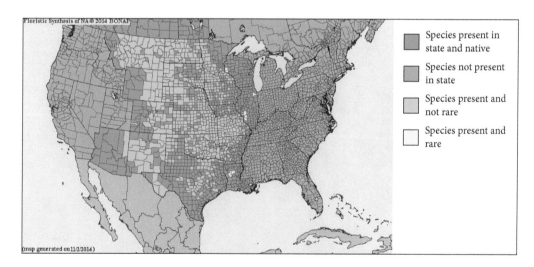

Figure 51. Map of U.S. counties with *Astragalus crassicarpus* collections.

Atriplex argentea Nutt.

- **Silverscale saltbush** or **Salt Plant** or **Orache**
- *čeewótš*
- *huhtaraawíš*

Figure 52. Silverscale saltbush, *Atriplex argentea,* was cooked and eaten as greens, and in a country that did not have much available salt, was appreciated for its saltiness. Photograph by Matt Lavin. Used with permission.

Gilmore gives two Arikara names for this plant. The first, *čeewótš,* means "little prairie sagewort", a diminutive derivation of *čeewa'út "Artemisia frigida"* above. The second name, *huhtaraawíš,* descriptively means "gray grass": "from *huún-u',* 'hay, grass' and *-taraawiiš* 'gray.'"

> This plant was used for greens and was cooked with other food to yield the salt which it contains. There are no salt marshes or other salt deposits in the Arikara country from which they could obtain this commodity in old times, so they made use of this plant to give savoriness to their food. It grows in alkali flats and takes into its own tissues much of the salt in heavy solution in that kind of soil. As the plant matures it becomes strongly saturated with salt so that it is very perceptible to the taste. They gathered quantities of the plant and placed some in the cooking pot with meat or other food. The salt in the tissues of the plant was dissolved out by cooking and absorbed by the other food. A supply of the plants would be gathered in early fall and preserved by drying for future use. The Arikara also mixed *Atriplex* with the fodder which they provided for their horses (G).

As a source of greens, it was considered similar to lambsquarters (*Chenopodium* species). A Smithsonian Institution specimen collected and annotated by Gilmore shows the material used, NMAI #122977.

Ella Waters commented (rec. ca. 1979) that the leaves of this plant "were dried, crushed or pounded into a powder, and then rubbed on spider bites to cure them" (Parks 1970–1997).

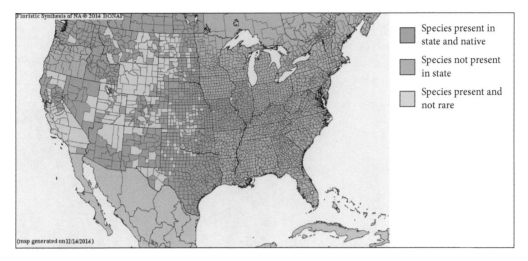

Figure 53. Map of U.S. counties with *Atriplex argentea* collections.

Calamagrostis canadensis (Michx.) P. Beauv.
- **Bluejoint**
- *katahtawáx*

Figure 54. The grass, bluejoint, *Calamagrostis canadensis*, had very sharp blades which were used to scrape cataracts off of the eyeball. Photograph by Matt Lavin. Used with permission.

The Arikara name literally means "rough green grass", comprised of *kataán-u'* "green grass" + *tawaax* "rough".

Ella Waters (rec. 1972) described this type of grass as "rough and sharp. The blades were used in treating trachoma and cataracts. An old woman would scrape the eyeball with the blade, the edge of which is very sharp. The blades were also used for cutting more generally" (Parks 1970–1997).

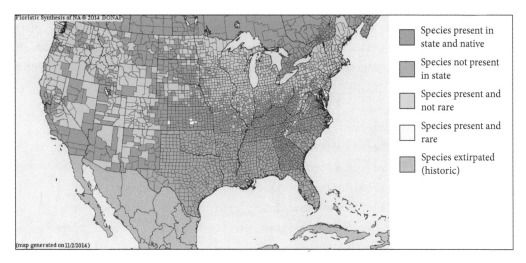

■	Species present in state and native
■	Species not present in state
■	Species present and not rare
□	Species present and rare
■	Species extirpated (historic)

Figure 55. Map of U.S. counties with *Calamagrostis canadensis* collections.

Calamovilfa longifolia (Hook) Scribn.

- **Sand Grass** or **Prairie Sandreed**
- *pakUsčiíšu'*
- *pákUs*

Figure 56. Prairie sandreed, *Calamovilfa longifolia,* stems were used as a pipe cleaner. Photograph by Michael Haddock. Used with permission.

The two Arikara names are related: *pákUs* is a basic stem that nowadays also refers to "oats". This use is probably an extension from a reference to the chaff or seeds of Sand Grass. The name *pakUsčiíšu'* is a compound of *pákUs* plus *čiiš-u'* "bone", the compound also referring to "straw" or "chaff".

> The stalks of this grass, when headed out, were used as an honor badge in a similar manner as eagle feathers were used. The stalk of this grass is the badge of one who, in a scouting party, has entered the camp of an enemy alone and has killed one or more. One entitled to this honor, wears attached to his hair, one stalk of this grass for each enemy he has killed under these circumstances. The stem of this grass, after leaves and tops are removed, is also used as a cleaner for pipe stems (G).

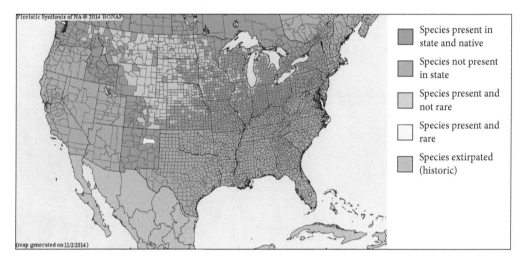

Figure 57. Map of U.S. counties with *Calamovilfa longifolia* collections.

Celastrus scandens L.

- **American bittersweet** or **Bittersweet**
- *načiikaahUxwáhAt*, in reference to the plant
- *čiRAhwáko'*, in reference to the berry

Figure 58. The seeds of bittersweet, *Celastrus scandens,* were used inside dried gourds as rattles. Photograph by Michael Haddock. Used with permission.

According to Gilmore, "The Arikara name, [*Najikahwa*], is derived from *načiikúxtš*, 'gourd', because the seeds of the bittersweet were used in the gourd-shell to make the sacred rattles for religious ceremonies" (G). Ella Waters (rec. 1976) described the *čiRAhwáko'* as an "orange berry that pops open in winter," while William Deane (rec. 1975) commented that "the orange winter berry was bitter and not eaten" (Parks 1970–1997).

Gilmore's transcription of the plant is tentatively interpreted as *načiikaahUxwáhAt*, which would mean literally "red drinking wood" (*rak-* "wood" + *čiikaa* "drink" + *-hux* "-ing" + *-wahat* "red") but could be more directly based on the name for *Smilax*, *načiikaáhUx*. Both the names of *Celastrus* and *Smilax* appear to be possibly related to the word for "gourd", as asserted by Gilmore in the above quote, although there are some irregularities there. An association with gourds used as drinking vessels could explain the etymology based on *čiikaa* "drink".

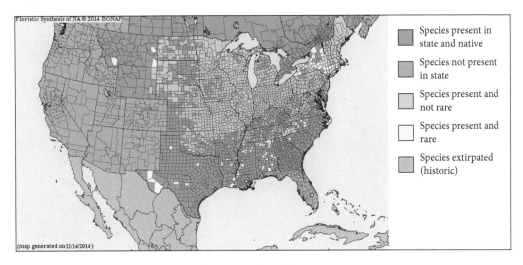

Figure 59. Map of U.S. counties with *Celastrus scandens* collections.

Chenopodium album L.

- **Goosefoot** or **Lambsquarters**
- *hawaxtaátu'*
- *kaxkaraní*

Figure 60. These young shoots of lamb's quarter, *Chenopodium album*, were cooked as greens, often being harvested as friendly weeds in the corn fields. Photograph by Kelly Kindscher.

Two Arikara names are applied to *Chenopodium album*: *hawaxtaátu'* is also used as a generic reference to "weeds". The second name *kaxkaraní* is a descriptive composition "from *kaáx-u'* 'leg' and -*karaniin* 'spotted', i.e. 'spotted leg,' or 'striped leg', from the coloring of the stem or leg of this plant."

> When any of the tasty goosefoot or lambsquarters species were young and tender, they were cooked as greens. They were also seasoned with suet, alkali salt, or cooked with the salt plant, *Atriplex argentea*, which grows on the salt flats and accumulates salt which would give it and what it is cooked with, a salty flavor (G).

Lambsquarters was one of the troublesome weeds in the Arikara cornfields (see others listed under *Asclepias syriaca*), but according to SteštAhkáta it was "not altogether bad as they were good for food as greens" (Melvin R. Gilmore Papers, Box 3, Field Notebooks).

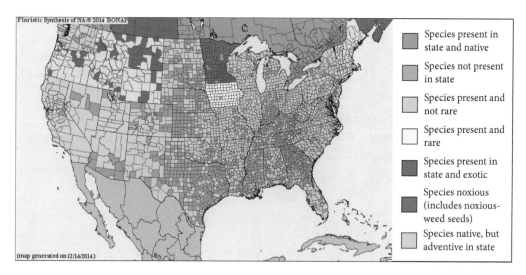

Figure 61. Map of U.S. counties with *Chenopodium album* collections.

Cirsium undulatum (Nutt.) Spreng.

- **Wavyleaf Thistle** or **Thistle**
- *neskoóčI*

Figure 62. The down, found associated with the dried seeds in wavyleaf thistle, *Cirsium undulatum,* heads were used for decorative material on garments. Photograph by Kelly Kindscher.

The Arikara name *neskoóčI* is a simple participle meaning "the sharp ones", which is "in reference to the sharp prickles on the plant" (G).

The down of thistles was used in ancient time for decorative materials on garments. For this purpose the thistle down was dyed and twisted into a fine yarn to use in embroidery in a similar manner as porcupine quills were used and as moose hair was used by the Indians of eastern Canada.

> Thistle stalks were used by those who were fasting to keep themselves awake while holding their vigils. They placed thistle stalks about themselves so that if they should fall asleep they would fall upon the thistle stalks and so be awakened (G).

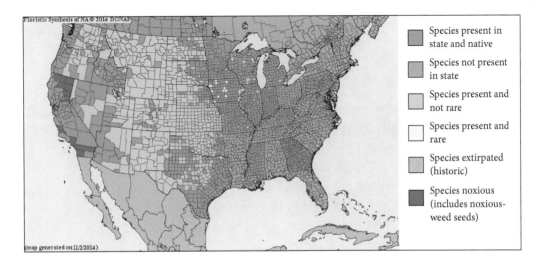

Figure 63. Map of U.S. counties with *Cirsium undulatum* collections.

Clematis ligusticifolia Nutt.

- **Virgin's bower** or **Western white clematis**
- *pAxkaásu'*

Figure 64. The white flowers of Virgin's bower, *Clematis ligustifolia,* become feathery white plumed fruits which were used by children in dress-up play and games. Photograph by Kelly Kindscher.

"The name *pAxkaásu'* means 'white hair'" (G), or more literally, "gray head": *páx-u'* "head" + *kaas* "be gray".

The vines of *Clematis* with their bunches of feathery white plumed fruits were used by children in play. They would attach them to their heads in the manner of a wig to look like the white hair of old persons. Thus they 'played old person.' Also, boys 'played war dance' by putting garlands of this vine with its plumed fruits on their ankles as ornaments (G).

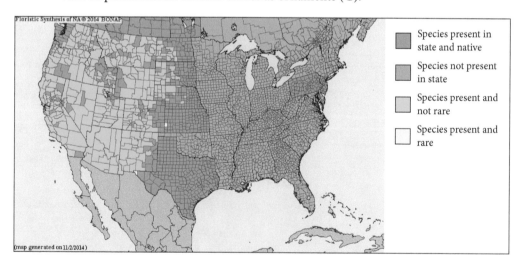

Figure 65. Map of U.S. counties with *Clematis ligustifolia* collections.

Cornus amomum Mill.

- **Silky dogwood**

Figure 66. The inner bark of silky dogwood, *Cornus amomum,* was used as part of a special tobacco smoking mix. Photograph by Peter Dziuk. Used with permission.

The inner bark of dogwood, was added to the dried leaves of bearberry (*Arctostaphylos uva-ursi*) and the leaves of the special tobacco (*Nicotiana quadrivalvis*) that the Arikara cultivated for its use as an important part of the smoking mix called *kinnikinnick* (Gilmore 1926b).

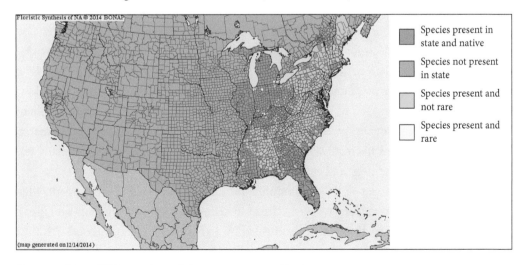

Figure 67. Map of U.S. counties with *Cornus amomum* collections.

Cornus sericea L.

- **Red Osier Dogwood** or **Kinnikinnick**
- formerly *Cornus stolonifera*
- *uuxapáhAt*, in reference to the tree
- *čiRAhkás*, in reference to the fruit

Figure 68. The inner bark of red osier dogwood, *Cornus sericea*, was the regionally-preferred dogwood species to use in a special tobacco smoking mix. Photograph by Matt Lavin. Used with permission.

The Arikara name of the tree translates to "red boxelder": *uuxaák-u'* "boxelder" + *-pahat* "red". The berry's name literally means "gray berry", based on their light color: *čiran-* "contained liquid, berry" + *kaas* "gray".

"The inner bark of this species was used for smoking in the same way as that of *Cornus amomum*" (G). According to Ella Waters (rec. ca. 1979), "the outer bark was scraped off first, and discarded. It was then the second layer that was scraped off and dried for use as kinnikinnick tobacco" (Parks 1970–1997). Gilmore also recorded that "the bitter somewhat acidulous berries of this shrub were eaten by the Arikaras as a remedy for huskiness of the voice" (G).

In a traditional Coyote Story recited by Lillian Brave (Parks 1991a:856–858), *sčiríhtš*, Coyote, performs a good deed for a group of *uuxapáhAt* "Dogwood trees". After being tricked into eating both Jerusalem Artichokes (*tšuúxIt*) and rose hips (*páhAt*), Coyote's rectum is left bleeding from all of the irritations the plants have caused (see the respective entries below). He then comes upon a stand of Dogwood saplings that are still young and green and have noticed his bleeding. Coyote agrees to rub his blood upon them to make them red, as mature trees. Although he ruins his rectum in the process, the artichokes and rose hips finally take pity on him for the good deed and cease their torment.

The importance of *uuxapáhAt* "kinnikinnick" for tobacco (*nanoóxu'*) is offhandedly illustrated in another recorded story, told by Alfred Morsette, in which a young man who breaks his leg while on the warpath is pitied and healed by a good-humored *tsAhunúxu'* "Scalped Man". After spending some time with the Scalped Man, the boy goes to visit his village and family, to let them know he is still alive. Even though he could choose just to remain in his village, the boy acts honorably and returns to the Scalped Man with prized gifts, including *uuxapáhAt* "tobacco/kinnikinnick" to thank him for healing him. In gratitude for this deed, the Scalped Man blesses the boy with his healing powers, and the boy is able to return to his village as a doctor (Parks 1991a:437–439).

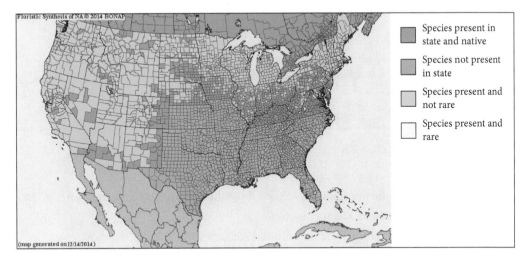

Figure 69. Map of U.S. counties with *Cornus sericea* collections.

Crataegus spp.

- **Hawthorn**
- *skačítA*

Figure 70. The thorns on the stems of the hawthorne, *Crataegus mollis,* were used as awls. Photograph by Michael Haddock. Used with permission.

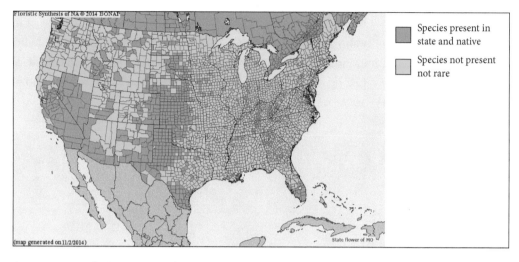

Figure 71. Map of U.S. counties with *Crataegus* collections.

The Arikara name may be interpreted as either "branching sharpness" or "sharp on top": *iska* "sharp" + *čita* "branching, forked" or "on top".

Parks (1970–1997) records from an unnoted Arikara speaker that "the thorns were used as awls. The berries were not eaten."

Cucurbita foetidissima Kunth

- **Missouri Gourd** or **Wild Gourd, Buffalo Gourd**
- *wahUxkásu'* lit. "squash root/herb"
- *načiikúxtš*

Figure 72. The pulverized root of the buffalo gourd (*Cucurbita foetidissima*) was used as an important medicine, even though the plant only occurred several hundred miles to the south. Photograph by Kelly Kindscher.

The first Arikara name is derived from *WAhúx*, the general term for "squash" of any kind, compounded with *kás-u'*, the term for useful herbs and roots. This name is probably based on the medicinal uses of the wild gourd. The second name, *načiikúxtš*, of unclear etymology— although possibly based on a historical compound of *rak-* "wood" + *čiikaa* "drink" (plus the suffixes *-hux* "-ing" and *-tš* "little" if accurate)—may be used of gourds or for rattles, typically constructed from *Cucurbita*.

> This plant is not indigenous in the Arikara country, but they are acquainted with its medicinal uses, and they import it from the south. As among other tribes, the root of this plant is very highly prized as a remedy for almost all ills. Among many other uses, it is employed as a remedy for ulcers and old, obstinate sores. The dried root is pulverized very finely and dusted over the sores (G).

Note that this species is currently found no farther north than the south half of Nebraska, about 500 miles south!

> As a remedy for dropsy (edema, or inflammation and watery swelling), the dried root is finely pulverized and mixed in water to drink. At the same time the pulverized root mixed with the fat of a snapping turtle is applied as an ointment to reduce the swelling and inflammation (G).

Ella Waters (rec. ca. 1979) states that the "seeds were put inside of [*načiikúxtš*] for use as rattles in rituals." Alice White Bear (rec. 1972) specifies that the rattles made from gourds were "used by medicine men" (Parks 1970–1997).

Angela Plante (rec. 1987, 1996), along with Lillian Brave (rec. 1987), described a plant which they could not identify that matches the description of *Cucurbita foetidissima*:

> the long root was said to be shaped like a human body, the length of a boy. It grew in South Dakota. Parts of the root seen as, e.g. arms or legs, were used to treat the corresponding body parts of a person. One of these roots is said to have been found by two medicine men near Shields, ND in the late 19th or early 20th century.

They attributed this description—perhaps erroneously—to the Arikara name *sačiínatA* [*Yucca glauca*], another plant with a large root not regularly found in the area of the Fort Berthold Indian Reservation in North Dakota.

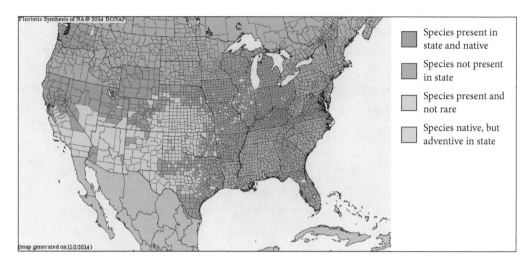

Figure 73. Map of U.S. counties with *Cucurbita foetidissima* collections.

Cyclachaena xanthiifolia (Nutt.) Fresen.

- called *Iva xanthifolia* by Gilmore
- **Marsh elder** or **Carelessweed** or **Giant Sumpweed**
- *hawaxtaátu'*

Figure 74. The young plants and tender leaves of marsh elder, *Cyclachaena xanthiifolia*, were cooked as greens. Photograph by Matt Lavin. Used with permission.

The name *hawaxtaátu'* is used generically to refer to "weeds", as well as referring to lambsquarters (see *Chenopodium album* above).

The Arikaras say they formerly used this plant for potherb while it was young and tender. They cooked it as greens seasoned with alkali salt and suet. They said it tasted somewhat like string beans. Even when older all sufficiently tender parts were so cooked and eaten.

Having no alkali deposits in their country, they often made use of the salts deposited by evaporation in alkali flats. For this purpose, the white dust was swept up and placed in vessels and dissolved out in water. As the salts were taken into solution, the earthy matter was deposited as a sediment and after settling the salt solution was poured off into vessels and used as required in cooking (G).

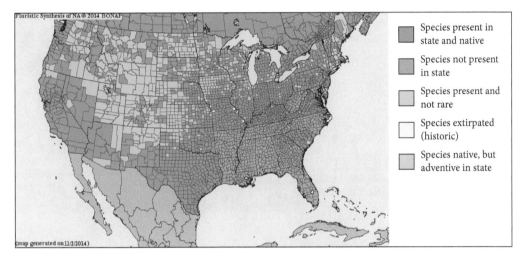

Figure 75. Map of U.S. counties with *Cyclachaena xanthiifolia* collections.

Dalea sp.

- **Prairie clover**
- *kAstsAhané*
- *kAstAhané*

Figure 76. The sweet root of white prairie clover, *Dalea candida,* was eaten with relish by children. Photograph by Peter Dziuk. Used with permission.

The Arikara name literally translates to "sweet root" or "root with a good tasting juice": *kás-u'* "root, herb" + *-tsahaneer* "be a sweet-tasting liquid", or *-tahaneer* "be sweet-tasting".

Prairie clover roots were "eaten with relish by children" (G). This species is most likely *Dalea candida* due to it being known for having a sweet root (Kindscher 1987).

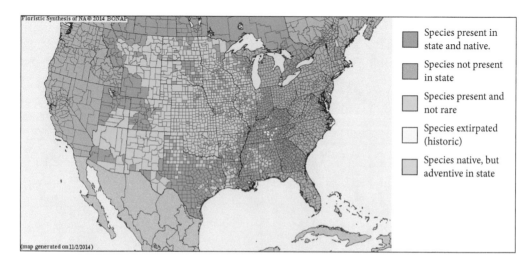

Figure 77. Map of U.S. counties with *Dalea candida* collections.

Echinacea angustifolia Moench

- called *Brauneria angustifolia* by Gilmore
- **Echinacea, Blacksamson echinacea** or **Purple coneflower**
- *šapitaahákUx, šapitaaRAhákUx*
- *kAskatít*, lit. "black herb"

Figure 78. A single stem of *Echinacea angustifolia* (narrow-leaf purple coneflower) showing off its sunset red cone and pale purple petals, was an important medicinal plant, and one of the important medicines that was shared with Lewis and Clark when they visited on their expedition. Photograph by Kelly Kindscher.

The Arikara name, *šapitaahákUx*, means "hand spinner": *íš-u'* "hand" + *apitaahak* "whirl, spin" + *-hUx* "-er". Another attested name, *kAskatít*, is composed of *kás-u'* "herb, root" + *katiit* "black".

> It is so named from a children's game called twirling, in which one cone-flower stalk is held horizontally in hand and another is whirled vertically upon the first, the two stalks being in contact at the heads. Children played at twirling one stalk of the plant over another, the cones making contact of one stalk with the other. The play is a sort of sleight-of-hand or play of knack or skill. The penalty for failure in the act is to be chased and beaten by the other players with the spring stalks of the plants (G).

This plant was the most important medicinal plant of Plains Indians, and used as a heal-all for colds, flu, rabies, other sickness, and rattlesnake bite (Gilmore 1977; Kindscher 1992).

The macerated (water-softened/chewed) root (method of grinding and dosage not given) of *Echinacea* was "used as an antidote for snake bite and other venomous bites and stings and poisonous conditions" by all the Indians of the Upper Missouri River region (Gilmore 1977). In addition, these Indians used echinacea "for more ailments than any other plant" (Gilmore 1913b).

Ella Waters (rec. ca. 1979) describes the use of *Echinacea*: "the root was used for treating toothaches, as it would numb the gums." William Deane, Jr. adds of its medicinal uses (rec. ca. 1975) that "it could also be used for treating earaches: a bunch of roots, about 12 inches long apiece, would be tied together and placed over hot coals. The person with the earache would then hold his ear over the resulting smoke." Ella Waters also comments that, "it was also used to protect oneself from others' bad medicine. (A dancer, for instance, will keep a piece of Echinacea root in his mouth to protect himself from other, jealous dancers)" (Parks 1970–1997).

Also there is an account from the explorers Lewis and Clark, who when traveling up the Missouri River, visited an Arikara village (that was located in northern South Dakota today). They continued up the river and stayed near a Mandan village (in North Dakota today) during the winter of 1804. When they were at the Mandan village, an English trader of the North West Company arrived from Assiniboine River outpost in Canada. He visited with William Clark and told him on December 16, 1804 about *E. angustifolia* root as "the cure of a Mad Dog". Clark wrote in his journal (in quaint language) on February 28, 1805 that in addition to its use for rabies, it also was used for snake bite and other ailments:

> this root is found on high lands and asent of hills, the way of useing it is to Scarify the part when bitten to chu or pound an inch or more if the root is Small, and applying it to the bitten part renewing it twice a Day. The bitten person in not to chaw or Swallow any of the Root for it might have contrary effect (Journals of the Lewis and Clark Expedition 2005).

Merriwether Lewis also shipped echinacea roots back East from the Great Plains. From their Mandan village camp, he discussed *E. angustifolia* in his note that accompanied a botanical specimen—a "parcel of its roots, and seeds to President Thomas Jefferson"—which was unfortunately lost. He commented in these notes written on April 3, 1805, that an Arikara chief, who had accompanied them from his village up the river to the Mandan village, had told him that the root "pounded in either green or dryed state makes an excellent poltice for swellings or soar throat" (Journals of the Lewis and Clark Expedition 2005). See also Kindscher 2016.

Figure 79. Map of U.S. counties with *Echinacea angustifolia* collections.

Eleagnus commutata Bernh. Ex Rydb.

- called *E. argentea* by Gilmore
- **Silverberry** or **Silver-berry bush**
- *nataraakaapaačíšU*, lit. "We (who are) are poor"

Figure 80. The dried leaves of silverberry, *Eleagnus commutatus*, were used to make a hot tea. Photograph by Matt Lavin. Used with permission.

The Arikara name, *nataraakaapaačíšU*, translates literally as 'we who are poor,' [a participle based on the stative verb *kaapaačiš* 'be poor or pitiful']. This name is probably due to the legend connected with the use of the leaves of this shrub to make a pleasant hot beverage tea (G).

Albert Simpson, an Arikara elder, told Melvin Gilmore in August 1926, the following story:

One time there was famine among Arikara and other tribes. Some men were on an expedition. They sat down on a hill, hungry, thirsty and miserable. They heard a voice calling to them. 'Come down here.' The men looked at each other; finally one dared to go down. He found himself standing amid a clump of silverberry bushes. He heard the voice continuing, saying: 'I know your troubles, and I have been wishing for you to come so that I might do something for you. Take the leaves and make a drink of hot water.' They did so. When they came home with this divine gift the people were thankful and the priests made a ceremony of thanksgiving, offering smoke to the Four Quarters, to Mother Earth, and to *neešaánu' tʰnačitákUx* ['The Chief Above'] (Gilmore 1927c).

Gilmore collected the tea leaves and they are archived at the Smithsonian Institution, NMAI #122983, and a specimen of this plant collected by Gilmore from the Ft. Berthold Reservation is in the University of Michigan Anthropology Museum collections, #4000-1-6503. Gilmore also stated that: "the Arikaras learned of its use from the Chippewas, since coming into the northern country. An example of changing habits and adoption of new things with new environment" (Melvin R. Gilmore Papers, Box 3, Field Notebooks).

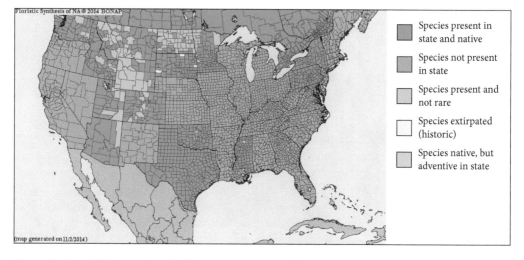

Species present in state and native

Species not present in state

Species present and not rare

Species extirpated (historic)

Species native, but adventive in state

Figure 81. Map of U.S. counties with *Eleagnus commutata* collections.

Equisetum sp.

- **Horsetail**

- *paakaruutaátu'*

Figure 82. The stems of horsetail, *Equisetum hyemale*, were used as a fodder for horses, and due to the high silica content in their stems, were also used for polishing wood and other objects. Photograph by Michael Haddock. Used with permission.

The Arikara name appears to mean "knee-crease stalk": *paá-u'* "knee" + *-karuu* "wrinkled, creased" + *taát-u'* "plant, stem, stalk". Such a name is undoubtedly based on the corrugation joints along the stalk. Gilmore provides the translation "horse cheek plant", although this does not completely work etymologically. His interpretation is possibly a reanalysis—or "folk etymology"—based on the foraging behavior of horses, sticking their snouts in the grass.

> Areas in the river valleys abounding with *Equisetum* were considered the most valuable pasture grounds for their horses. They even gathered quantities of this plant as forage for the horses kept for immediate use at their villages." It is "[o]ne of the principal horse foods, like oats.

> There is a considerable deposit of silica in the tissues of these plants, and the stems are corrugated. Because of these properties, they are used for finely abrasive material for polishing objects, just as emery paper is used by White people (G).

Figure 83. Map of U.S. counties with *Equisetum* species collections.

Ericameria nauseosa (Pall. ex Pursh) G.L. Nesom & Baird

- called *Chrysothamnus graveolens* by Gilmore
- **Rubber rabbitbrush** or **Rabbitbrush**
- *naNAsaraawíš*, lit. "gray woods"

Figure 84. The flowering tops of rabbitbrush, *Ericameria nauseosa*, were used for treating the saddle ores on horses. Photograph by Craig Freeman. Used with permission.

The Arikara name is a simple descriptive compound: *rak- ~ haak-* "wood" + *ran-* "plural" + *taraawiiš* "gray".

"A wash was made from the tops for treating saddle-sores on horses. Also, when a favorite war or race horse is lathered from running the sweat and dirt are washed off with hot water using this plant for a brush" (G). Also, a specimen of this plant collected by Gilmore from the Ft. Berthold Reservation is in the University of Michigan Anthropology Museum collections, #4000-1-6502.

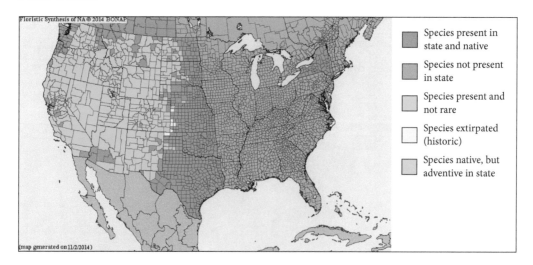

Figure 85. Map of U.S. counties with *Ericameria nauseosa* collections.

Erysimum asperum (Nutt.) DC.

- **Western wallflower**
- *kunawaáxA*

Figure 86. The bright yellow flowering heads, tops and leaves of western wallflower, *Erysimum asperum,* were pulverized and used to treat cuts, wounds and poison ivy. Photograph by Kelly Kindscher.

This plant was

> the main medicine used for gunshot and arrow wounds. Boiled to make a washing for the wounds or sores, and pulverized (tops, leaves and flowers) and powder dusted on after the washing. And mixed with other plants for external use on cuts and all sores and sores from poisoning in the woods (G)

(most likely sores from poison ivy, *Toxicodendron rydbergii* [Small ex Rydb.] Greene).

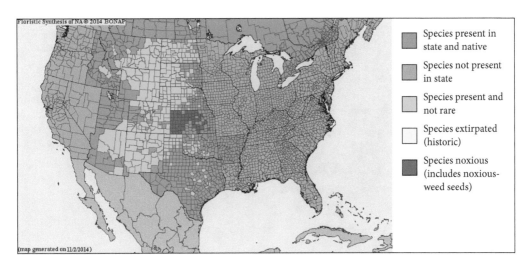

Figure 87. Map of U.S. counties with *Erysimum asperum* collections.

Fraxinus pennsylvanica Marshall

- **Green ash** or **ash**
- *čiNIhnaáku'*

Figure 88. The wood of green ash, *Fraxinus pennsylvanica*, was prized for making bowls, which served as the mortar for grinding medicines. Photograph by Peter Dziuk. Used with permission.

Gilmore reported that

> The bark of the ash tree was used to make a deer decoy for hunting. A man who died here ten years ago was badly hurt by a buck deer running up to him and tossing him or pushing him with his antlers. They come suddenly at the sound (due to its effectiveness). Also the wood of ash was prized for making medicine bowls (G).

Ella Waters (ca. 1979) adds that "an ash log was also used for the mortar in pounding or grinding medicines" (Parks 1970–1997).

One of the traditional, pre-reservation Arikara villages was named *ČiNIhnahtákUx* "Ash Perched Upon a Hill" (Parks 2001:376).

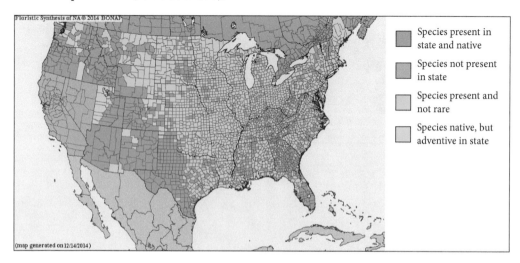

Figure 89. Map of U.S. counties with *Fraxinus pennsylvanica* collections.

Galium triflorum Michx.

- **Fragrant bedstraw**
- *haaNUtwaraakAhaanaáNUx*

Figure 90. The fragrant bedstraw, *Galium triflorum,* was used as a woman's perfume. Photograph by Peter Dziuk. Used with permission.

The Arikara name translates most literally to "hairy fragrant grass in the woods": *haanuút-u'* "native grass" + *waraa-* "forest" + *-kahaan* "fragrant" + *-raanux* "hairy". It may more directly mean "hairy sweetgrass", based on the name for *Hierochloe odorata, haaNUtwaraakAhá'* (see below).

The plant was used for perfume. Objects that Gilmore sent the Heye Museum in New York from the Arikara Reservation in September 1923 included this plant with a label: "Specimen of 'women's perfume.'" Ella Waters (rec. ca. 1979) quotes her father on *Galium triflorum* and *Hierochloe odorata: inaáni' šití'A*: "They are brothers/sisters," using the Arikara term *inaáni'* refers to siblings of the same sex, i.e., a brother of a male or or a sister of a female (Parks 1970–1997).

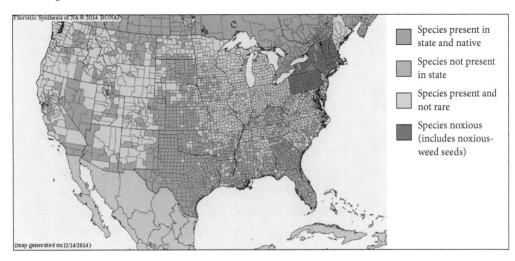

Figure 91. Map of U.S. counties with *Galium triflorum* collections.

Glycyrrhiza lepidota Pursh.

- **American licorice** or **Wild licorice**
- *piira'aátUx*
- *kAspiira'aátUx*, lit. "herb bur"
- *piira'aatUxtanáha'*, lit. "buffalo bur"
- *kAskatarí*, lit. "rapid herb"

Figure 92. The wild licorice (*Glycyrrhiza lepidota*), had many uses, including as a medicine for diarrhea, colds, and sore throats. Photograph by Craig Freeman. Used with permission.

The first name, *piira'aátUx*, appears to include the lexical root *piíra-u'* "child, baby". The second part of this name, *aát-hUx*, may be historically associated with burs in and of itself, considering a partial Pawnee cognate *aat-kirit* "sandbur" (literally "bur-eye"). The second name compounds this first name with *kás-u'* "herb, root". The third name compounds the first name with *tanáha'* "buffalo".

> The burrs of wild licorice were used to clean old sores by abrasion. They were also used in the old time in the process of tattooing, being used as an abrasive for clearing off the epidermis before applying the tattooing needles. Incidentally, porcupine quills were used also in the old time for pricking the pigment into the skin in tattooing.

> The Arikara name, *kAskatarí*, is compounded from *kás-u'*, 'herb, root,' and *-katariin* 'rapid, fast,' because if cut off, it shoots up new growth again quickly. And wild licorice was recognized as a problematic weed in corn fields along the river. The root is used medicinally for several ailments. For diarrhea, the dried root was pulverized and put into hot water and steeped. A half cupful is a dose. As a remedy for hoarseness and any trouble of the

vocal organs a piece of the root was chewed and retained in the mouth and the juice mixed with saliva was swallowed. It was also a remedy for colds and all bronchial trouble. It was given to horses as a remedy for colic. Also, insect galls from the wild rose, *Rosa arkansana*, were both dried and mixed by pounding, boiled, strained, and also drunk as a remedy for sore throat (G).

In addition, "ripe seeds were powdered and mixed with tepid water, and applied to the top of the head for headache, 'bad dreams,' nightmare, etc." (G).

As an additional usage, Ella Waters (rec. 1976) reported that "wild licorice, together with root of corn, were pounded, then put in the mouth when singing," (Parks 1970–1997) to help soothe the vocal chords.

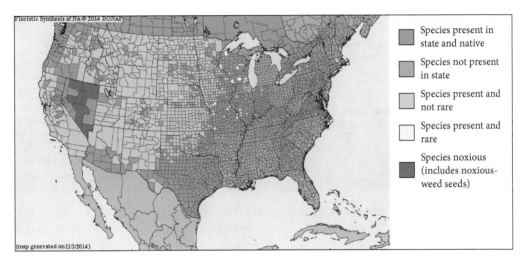

Figure 93. Map of U.S. counties with *Glycyrrhiza lepidota* collections.

Grindelia squarrosa (Pursh) Dunal

- **Curlycup gumweed, Gummy weed, Sticky-head,** or **Tar-weed**
- *pAxčiisiísu' (taátu'),* lit. "filthy head (plant)"

Figure 94. The sticky heads (with white sap in this picture) of curly cup gumweed, *Grindelia squarrosa,* were used to stop wounds from bleeding and as an adhesive for attaching feathers to arrow shafts. Photograph by Michael Haddock. Used with permission.

The Arikara name, *pAxčiisiísu' taátu',* or just *pAxčiisiís-u'* or *pAxčiísis,* is a composite of *páx-u',* "head", and *čiisiís,* "gummy filth". Gilmore's transcription also includes *taát-u'* "plant, stem" and a noun suffix *-u'* at the end of *pAxčiisiis-.*

> The plant is of the family called composites, the family which includes daisies and sunflowers. The bracts under the flower head are closely imbricated [shingled] and are sticky with a resinous exudation. The ray flowers are bright yellow. The round head with its spreading yellow rays suggests, to the Indian beholder, a warrior's head crowned with a brilliant yellow feather war bonnet. And because of the stickiness of this resinous head it can become dirty and is compared to the sticky, dirty head of the one who has neglected washing and caring for his hair, hence the name, which mean (sticky-dirty-head-plant).

Young women sometimes made use of the resinous heads of this plant in making their toilet [dressing or grooming oneself] for some public entertainment when they gave particular attention to their appearance. They rubbed it over their hair, after they had combed it the way they wanted it to stay, the resinous heads of this plant in order to make their hair lie in place as they wanted it.

Arrow makers used the resin of this plant to attach the plumes to their arrows. They would take a bunch of these flowers and would run their sinew thread through them to gum it as a shoemaker makes a 'waxed-end' of his sewing thread by passing it through a ball of shoemaker's wax. The Arikara arrow-maker then, with his gummed sinew thread wrapped the plumes very securely to the arrow-shaft.

Grindelia heads were used in conjunction with the pulverized root of *Amorpha microphylla* before mentioned, to make a styptic for wounds (to stop their bleeding). Even when the *Grindelia* heads are dried they can be used for this purpose by moistening them with water, then their adhesive quality is recovered (G).

According to a note in Parks (1970–1997), given by an uncertain Arikara speaker, "*Grindelia squarrosa* was also used to treat venereal diseases in men. The plant was boiled in water and the solution was then used to wash the infected area."

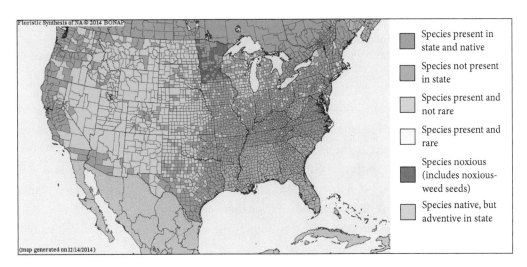

Figure 95. Map of U.S. counties with *Grindelia squarrosa* collections.

Helianthus annuus L.

- **Common sunflower** or **Sunflower**
- *sčiriNAhkataanawí'u'*, *čiriNAhkataanawí'u'*, in reference to the plant and flower
- *aánu'*, in reference to the seed.

Figure 96. The seeds of the wild common sunflower, *Helianthus annuus,* were inferior in size, but superior in taste to the ones grown in fields and were collected for food and their flavor. Photograph by Craig Freeman. Used with permission.

The two names for the plant, although differing only in the initial consonant, suggest two different etymologies. The interpretation given to Gilmore is that the name means "resembling a yellow eye", which matches the second variant: *čiriík-u'* "eye" + *-rahkataan* "yellow" + *awi* "like". However, the first variant—with the /s/—appears to mean "resembling a yellow wolf/ coyote", the first element being *sčirin-* "wolf, coyote". Note the first variant was documented as also applying to Maximilian sunflower (*H. maximiliani* Schrad.).

The Arikara term for the sunflower seed sounds the same as the word for "tooth": *aánu'*, although this may be coincidental.

> The flower heads of sunflower were used in play by little boys for war bonnets, which they resemble.

Sunflowers were grown for their seeds used as food and a source of cooking oil. One use of sunflower seeds was to make what was commonly called corn balls [*štípii'It*]. This article of food was composed of one part of parched sunflower seed ground to meal mixed with three parts parched sweet corn ground to meal. The sunflower meal and cornmeal were mixed and pressed together into spherical cakes and were very much liked by the Arikara, and also other tribes who cultivated corn and sunflowers. Wild sunflower seeds were also used for food. Arikara people told me that though the seeds of the wild are inferior in size they are superior in flavor (G).

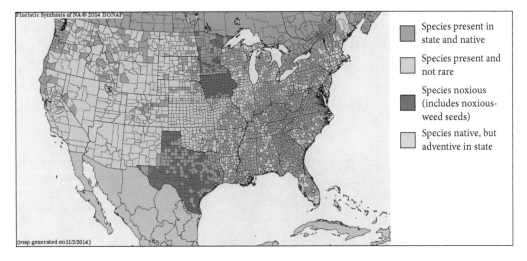

Figure 97. Map of U.S. counties with *Helianthus annuus* collections.

Helianthus tuberosus L.

- **Jerusalem artichoke**
- *tšuúxIt,* in generic reference to the plant or referring to the tuber
- *tšuuxIstaátu',* in specific reference to the plant

Figure 98. The tubers of the Jerusalem artichoke, *Helianthus tuberosus,* were an important food and also part of a colorful Arikara story related to the flatulence of a coyote who has eaten them. Photograph by Kelly Kindscher.

The general Arikara term for *Helianthus tuberosus*, the tuber or the plant, is *tšuúxIt*. The second name, compounded with *taát-u'* "plant, stalk", is used for the plant itself when clarification is needed. The tubers of this plant were used for food, commonly eaten raw as a salad, or cooked (roasted). They were also recognized as a problematic weed in corn fields along the river.

Parks (1991a) includes two versions of a humorous Coyote story, as told by William Deane, Jr. and Lillian Brave, respectively. In both stories, the *tšuúxIt* goad Coyote into cat ing them. Then, as he continues on his way, he is beset by increasingly explosive flatulence. Although he at first takes pleasure in the sensation, the farts soon begin to propel Coyote into the air, injuring him as he lands. He then seeks to anchor himself by taking hold of plants and other items. In Dan Hopkins' version (Parks 1991a:1258–1259), he finally takes hold of a rock, but ends up bashing his head upon it when he lands, explaining why the bones of coyotes are sometimes found next to rocks. In Lillian Brave's story (Parks 1991a:852–858), Coyote is further tricked and abused by *páhAstaátu'*, rose bushes, but he is finally spared when he performs a good deed, painting the *uuxapáhAt* dogwood saplings red with the blood from his injuries.

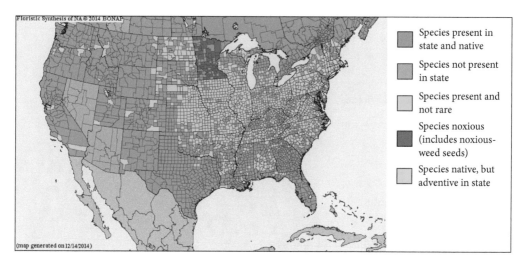

Figure 99. Map of U.S. counties with *Helianthus tuberosus* collections.

Hesperostipa spartea (Trin.) Barkworth

- called *Stipa spartea* by Gilmore
- **Porcupinegrass** or **Needle and thread grass**
- *piísus*

Figure 100. The stiff awn "stems" of the seeds of porcupinegrass, *Hesperostipa spartea*, horizontally attached in this photo, were bundled together into a hairbrush. Photograph by Craig Freeman. Used with permission.

The Arikara name of this grass, apparently not recorded by Gilmore, is the same as, and appears to derive from, the general term for "comb" or "hairbrush". It is also used for hay needles.

Gilmore wrote in his field notebook in July 1923:

> Stubby Horn and his wife from across the river were over and he came to my camp to see me. He told me of a number of games played by boys. I asked him to make sets of some of the objects used in such games, which he said he would do. I had gathered a quantity of needles of *Stipa spartea* and wished to have a hairbrush made from them. His wife took the needles and undertook to make brushes from them. I paid her $1.50 for 6.

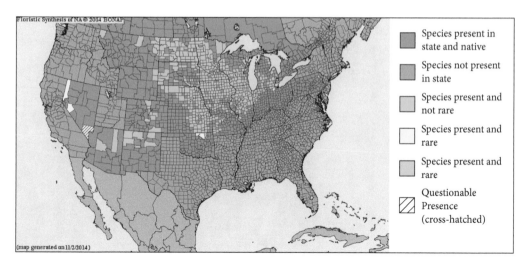

Figure 101. Map of U.S. counties with *Hesperostipa spartea* collections.

Figure 102. A hairbrush made from the long stiff awns of porcupine or needle and thread grass (both of these names also refer to these awns). These stiff awn pieces are bound together with a leather wrap. Gilmore had one of these traditional hairbrushes made for him in 1923. National Museum of the American Indian, Smithsonian Institution, Catalog Number 12/3024.

Heterotheca villosa (Pursh) Shinners

- called *Chrysopsis villosa* by Gilmore
- **Hairy False Golden Aster** or **Golden Aster**
- *napa'út*

Figure 103. The tops, leaves, and flower tops of golden aster, *Heterotheca villosa*, were boiled to make a wash to cure saddle sores on horses. Photograph by Matt Lavin. Used with permission.

"This is the gray plant with the yellow flowers. The tops, leaves, and inflorescences were boiled to make a wash to cure saddle galls on horses" (G).

Note that the same Arikara name is used for *Heterotheca villosa* as for *Artemisia longifolia* and *A. tridentata*, described above.

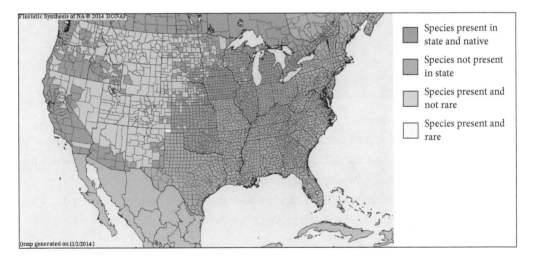

Species present in state and native

Species not present in state

Species present and not rare

Species present and rare

Figure 104. Map of U.S. counties with *Heterotheca villosa* collections.

Hierochloe odorata (L.) P. Beauv.

- **Sweetgrass**
- *haaNUtwaraakAhá'*

Figure 105. These vertical leaves of sweetgrass, *Hierochloe odorata*, were braided and used for smudging and as incense. Photograph by Rachel Liester. Used with permission.

The Sahnish name translates as "aromatic grass in the forest": *haanuút-u'* "grass" + *waraa-* "in the forest" + *-kahaan* "have a smell". See also the name of *Galium triflorum* above, which may be best translated as "hairy Sweetgrass (*Hierochloe odorata*)".

This plant was used for perfume (G) and braided for this purpose. As described in Parks (1970–1997), recorded from an uncertain Arikara speaker,

> sweetgrass was used to smudge pipes. It was also used in ceremonial rituals. The pipe was smudged before tobacco was put in its bowl. In the old days, a male dancer would smudge his outfit first, and then himself before putting his outfit on.

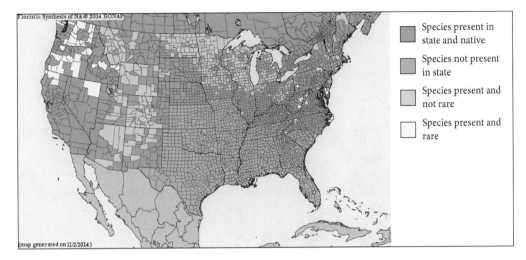

Figure 106. Map of U.S. counties with *Hierochloe odorata* collections.

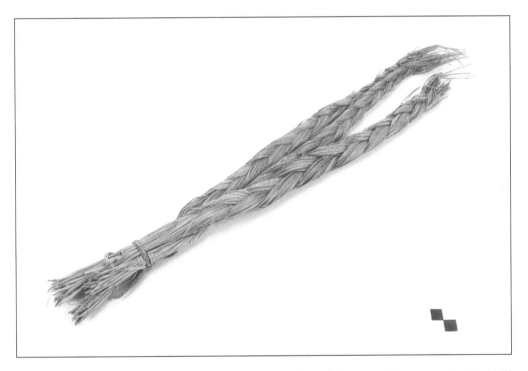

Figure 107. This sweetgrass braid was used as an incense and smudging material in ceremonies. The braid was collected by Melvin Gilmore when on the Fort Berthold Reservation in 1923. National Museum of the American Indian, Smithsonian Institution, Catalog Number 12/2995.

Juniperus horizontalis Moench

- **Creeping juniper** or **Ground cedar, Stunted cedar**
- *taWIsaakatóx*
- *kAhaanawičés*

Figure 108. The creeping juniper, *Juniperus horizontalis,* was used for both medicine and as incense. Photograph by Matt Lavin. Used with permission.

"The name, *taWIsaakatóx*, means 'flat cedar': *taWIsaák-u'* 'cedar' + -*katoox* 'flat'" (G). The name *kAhaanawičés* literally means "long smell": *kahaana* "smell" + *wi* "sitting" + *čees* "long".

Gilmore reported that "this species is used medicinally, and also for incense, in the manner as *J. virginiana*" (G). Ella Waters (rec. ca. 1979) describes how

> the needles were boiled and solution applied to sore or aching legs. The stunted cedar is a variety of cedar having short needles, not sharp, growing alongside other pine trees. It was used for incense in certain ceremonies (Parks 1970–1997).

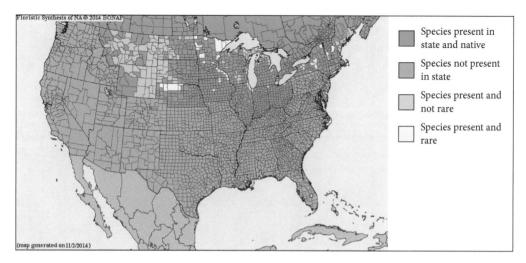

	Species present in state and native
	Species not present in state
	Species present and not rare
	Species present and rare

Figure 109. Map of U.S. counties with *Juniperus horizontalis* collections.

Juniperus virginiana L.

- **Red Cedar**
- *taWIsaáku'*

Figure 110. The small branches, mostly needles (leaves), of the red cedar, *Juniperus virginiana,* were important when used in tea as a remedy for chills and colds. The small branches were also burned and the smoke was important in ceremonies. Photograph by Craig Freeman. Used with permission.

Cedar berries were called *nakaánus*, also used for Chokecherries.

"This tree has an important place in religious ritualism. Its leaves and twigs were burned as incense in many ceremonies." Ella Waters (rec. ca. 1979) commented that: "This is the tree used ceremonially, known as Grandmother Cedar (*atíka'*)" (Parks 1970–1997).

It was also used in medicine as "a decoction of cedar leaves is drunk as a remedy for chills and colds, at the same time the whole body is subjected to a warm fumigation under a blanket, using hot vapor from cedar leaves." As a perfume, "cedar was used to pack away with clothing for its pleasant odor" (G).

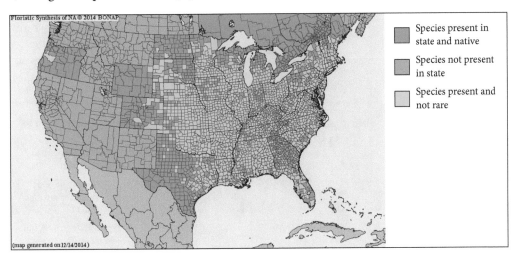

Figure 111. Map of U.S. counties with *Juniperus virginiana* collections.

Lactuca tatarica (L.) C.A. Mey.

- **Blue lettuce**
- *kAsiítu'*

Figure 112. The ground root of blue lettuce, *Lactuca tatarica,* was used to treat swelling, including for broken bones. Photograph by Ernie Marx. Used with permission.

The Arikara name is a compound meaning "feather root/herb": *kás-u'* "herb, root" + *hiít-u'* "feather".

> Used when green to roll up and used as a bath sponge or wash rag on children because it is soft to the skin in bathing, washing neck and ears. The root is also used for medicine for swellings from broken bones. The root, dried or fresh was ground to a fine powder and mixed with hot water to wash such swellings (G).

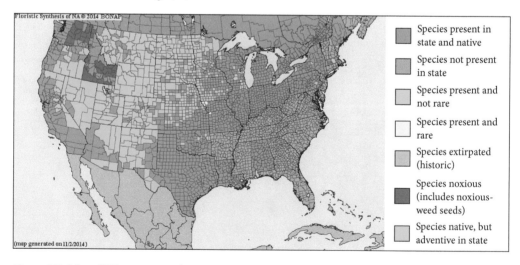

Figure 113. Map of U.S. counties with *Lactuca tatarica* collections.

Liatris spp.

- **Blazing star** or **Gayfeather**
- *čiškaruupáhAt* (?)

Figure 114. The bright purple spikes of blazing star *Liatris punctata,* was a phenological indicators, that is informing people that as the beautiful purple blazing stars were evident, then the Arikara's corn would be getting ripe, and it was time for a visit. Photograph by Craig Freeman. Used with permission.

The Arikara name that Gilmore records, [*Ciškarupa*], appears to mean "red withered head or bone", although there is some reservation in this interpretation. The word *čiíš-u'* regularly means "bone", but appears to refer to "head" elsewhere, as in *čiškookú'u'* "hat (bone/head-cover)". This appears to be modified by *karuu(x)* "withered", the absence of the final [x] being minimally attested elsewhere. Finally, the most likely interpretation of Gilmore's "*pa*" might be *-pahAt*, the oft attested "red" modifier. Gilmore appears to have recorded this word only once and no other documenters provide any alternative transcriptions by which to evaluate this form.

In Gilmore's publication called "Arikara Commerce" (Gilmore 1926a), he discussed how *Liatris* species were "phenological indicators that told the tribes when the Arikara corn was ripe." For this publication, he interviewed the elder, John Box in 1924 who stated: "At the time of green corn the agricultural tribes along the river, among whom the Arikaras were foremost, were sure to have many visitors from the Plains tribes." These tribes noted the time of the appearance of the blossoms of the blazing star (*Liatris scariosa* and *L. pycnostachya*). When these flowers came into bloom, they would say,

> Now the Arikaras' corn is coming into condition for eating. Let us go and visit them. So, they resorted to the villages of the Arikaras, bringing with them presents from the products of the natural resources of their own country and works of their own handicraft, and enjoyed feasts of green corn with their Arikara hosts. At this time, and again in the fall, when the ripe corn, beans and squashes and sunflower seeds were harvest[ed], foreign

tribes came to the Arikaras and other agricultural tribes and for many days engaged in mutual exchange of commodities.

Gilmore mentions two blazing star species, *L. scariosa* and *L. pycnostachya*, but *L. scariosa* is much to the east in North Dakota, so this is most likely *L. punctata* or *L. asper* which also occur in the North Dakota and the western Great Plains where summer bison hunting would likely occur.

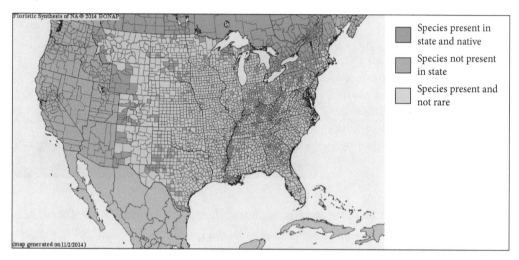

Figure 115. Map of U.S. counties with *Liatris species* collections.

Linum lewisii Pursh.

- **Lewis flax** or **Wild flax**
- *nakáxIš*, lit. "hard wood"
- *huhtanáha'*, lit. "buffalo grass"
- *piiRUxkátox*, lit. "bedbug":
- *huuNIškanítš*, lit. "meadow rue grass"

Figure 116. The stalks of the wild blue flax, *Linum lewisii,* had several uses as medicine. For one, they were ground fine, boiled and used as a diarrhea medicine. Photograph by Matt Lavin. Used with permission.

The first of the listed Arikara names translates as "hard wood": *rak- ~ haak-* "wood" + *-kaxiš* "hard". This same term is used for Tarragon (*Artemisia dracunculus*) above. The second name is a compound of *huún-u'* "grass" + *tanáha'* "buffalo". This latter name is undoubtedly associated with the plant's ceremonial usage described below. The third name given means "bed bug", or more literally "flat bug": *piíRUx* "bug" + *katoox* "flat". This name is no doubt due to the similarity in appearance of wild flax seeds to bed bugs. Finally, the fourth name is also due to similarity in appearance: *huún-u'* "grass" + *(I)škanítš* "meadow rue". Gilmore records that his consultant claims the name is based on the "likeness of the seeds" (G) between *Linum lewisii* and *Thalictrum*.

"The stalks of this plant were ground fine, boiled, and used for diarrhea. It was said that this use was learned by the Arikaras from the Chippewas" (G). In addition, the flower blossoms, when blue, were gathered and dried, then powdered to make poultice for burns.

Wild flax was used as an offering to the buffalo, or bison, when catching eagles. According to Red Bear, whom Gilmore interviewed in 1923,

> When men wished to catch eagles they looked for a likely place to make an eagle pit on some high, lonely rocky hill. Thus the pit was made. At another place, some distance away the eagle hunter made camp. At his camp he enshrined a buffalo skull, gathering a quantity of wild flax, he made of it a bed on which to lay his skull. In the mouth and eye sockets of the skull he stuffed wild flax also and made his prayers and sang his songs for the Spirit of the Buffalo to aid him to catch eagles.

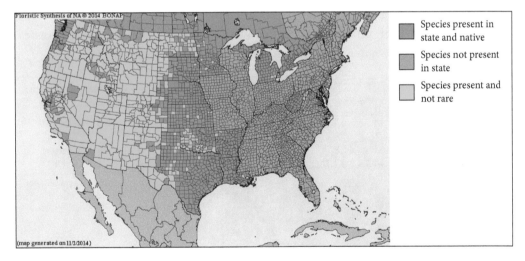

	Species present in state and native
	Species not present in state
	Species present and not rare

Figure 117. Map of U.S. counties with *Linum lewisii* collections.

Lomatium dissectum (Nutt.) Mathias & Constance

- **Bear root, Fat root, Fernleaf biscuitroot**
- *kAsAhíhtu'*, lit. "fat root"

Figure 118. The bear root, *Lomatium dissectum,* which occurred no closer than Montana, was an important medicine of the region and the Arikara burned the root and used the smoke from it to treat ear ache. Photograph by Robyn Klein. Used with permission.

The Arikara name translates as "fat root": *kás-u'* "herb, root" + *ahiht* "fat".

Both William Deane, Jr. (rec. ca. 1979) and Ella Waters (rec. 1977) comment on the greasiness of the root, while Alfred Morsette (rec. 1976) adds that it is sweet. Ella Waters further remarks that "the root is round, bulbous, extremely light weight, and about 2.5 inches in diameter. It grows in Montana and is eaten by bears." She also describes its medicinal use: "It is burned and the smoke used for an ear ache. The dried root was put on hot coals or embers. A person with an earache would put his or her ear over the smoke wafting upward" (Parks 1970–1997). This medicine was highly prized across the region and many tribes traveled for it, in this case as far as Montana. Other plants are also known as bear root, but this is the only fat root.

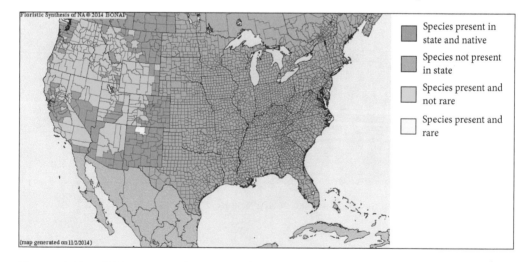

Figure 119. Map of U.S. counties with *Lomatium dissectum* collections.

Lonicera dioica L.

- **Limber honeysuckle**
- *načiikuxtAhkoóku'u'*,
  lit. "gourd cover"

Figure 120. The seeds of the limber honeysuckle, *Lonicera dioica*, were used as the noisemakers in rattles. Photograph by Craig Freeman. Used with permission.

The Arikara name appears to be composed of *načiikúx-tš* "gourd" + *-ran* "PL" + *kooku-u'* "covering".

Gilmore identifies this vine on separate occasions as Virginia creeper (*Parthenocissus vitacea*) and honeysuckle. The seeds from this plant are used as the noisemakers in rattles. Rattles were often made from dried gourds.

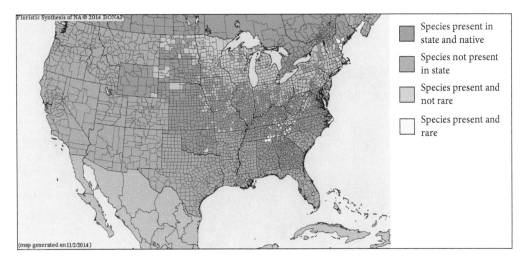

Figure 121. Map of U.S. counties with *Lonicera dioica* collections.

Lophophora williamsii (Lem. ex Salm-Dyck) J.M. Coult.

- **Peyote** or **Mescal**
- *kAsItkAhaánu'*, lit. "ear herb/root"
- *kásu'*, lit. "root, herb"
- *kunaá'u'*, lit. "medicine"

The most specific Sahnish name translates literally as "ear root/herb", *kás-u'* "root, herb" + *ItkAhaán-u'* "ear", describing the shape of the peyote button. When the context makes the reference apparent, the peyote button may simply be called *kás-u'* "herb", a term that is favored for medicinal and ceremonial plants, or *kunaá'u'* "medicine".

Arikara peyote buttons were collected by Gilmore in 1923 from his North Dakota trip that summer and

Figure 122. Peyote, *Lophophora williamsii*, was known and used on the Fort Berthold Reservation when Melvin Gilmore interviewed Arikara elders in the early 1920s. It was traded and brought up from southern Texas or Chihuahua. Photograph by Kelly Kindscher.

are archived at the Smithsonian Institution, NMAI #126173. Peyote is not a native plant, but is found in the wild in south Texas and in northern Mexico. Gilmore did not provide any other details on its use by the Arikara. Gilmore previously documented that peyote or "mescal" was introduced to the Omaha tribe from a tribal member who had visited an Oto man in Oklahoma who used it for both a religious practice and to cure alcoholism (Gilmore 1919). Gilmore also stated that he had been invited and attended "several mescal meetings in the Omaha tribe."

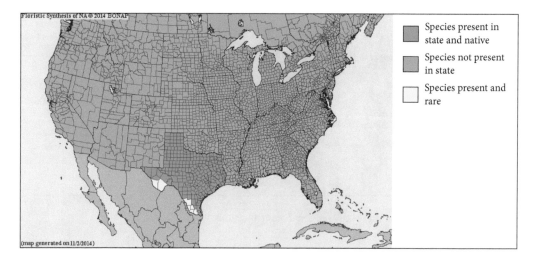

Figure 123. Map of U.S. counties with *Lophophora williamsii* collections.

Machaeranthera pinnatifida (Hook.) Shinners

- **Lacy tansy aster**
- *hItkaataátš*
- *naRAsaraawíšU*, lit. "the gray one"

Figure 124. The lacey tansy aster plant, *Machaeranthera pinnatifida*, was used as a horse medicine. Photograph by Michael Haddock. Used with permission.

The name recorded by Gilmore, *hItkaataátš*, also refers to "tallow, suet" as well as the stock of cattail and the pith of cottonwood logs that have been floating in the river. The second name that has been found to apply to Lacy tansyaster, *naRAsaraawíšU*, refers to a grayish color.

> When a horse has been exhausted in the chase of war and the expedition stops, they are rubbed up and this plant is mixed with cold water, and the horse is thrown down and this mixture is forced down his throat to stimulate and revive him (G).

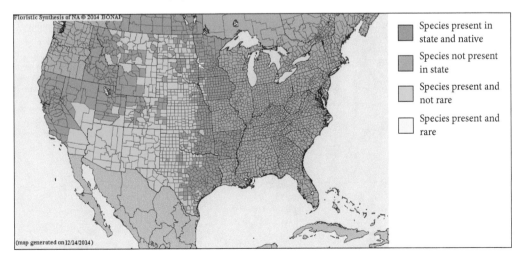

Figure 125. Map of U.S. counties with *Machaeranthera pinnatifida* collections.

Maclura pomifera (Raf.) C.K. Schneid.

- Osage orange

Figure 126. The wood of the Osage orange, *Maclura pomifera*, was the favorite bow wood as it was incredibly strong and light. It occurs hundreds of miles south of where the Arikara lived, so they traded with the Osage and others for it. Photograph by Michael Haddock. Used with permission.

John Bradbury reported when visiting the Arikara villages in 1809 that the Arikara made use of this imported wood for their bows used in hunting:

> The bows ... are made of a yellow wood, from a tree which grows on the Red River, and perhaps on the Arkansas. This wood is called *bois jaune*, or *bois d'arc*. I do not think the tree has yet been described, ... The fruit is as large as an apple, and is rough on the outside. It bleeds an acrid milky juice when wounded, and is call[ed] by the hunters the Osage orange. The price of a bow made from this wood at the Aricaras is a horse and a blanket. Many of the war clubs are made of the same kind of wood (Brackenridge 1814).

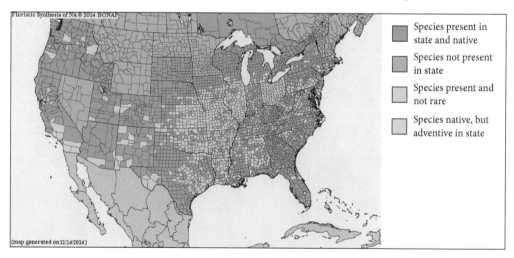

Figure 127. Map of U.S. counties with *Maclura pomifera* collections.

Mentha arvensis L.

- called *M. canadensis* by Gilmore
- **Wild mint**
- *šireéšu'*

When Gilmore was on the Ft. Berthold Reservation during late July, 1923, he "interviewed Mrs. Butcher and others at Clare Everett's house in regard to dye stuffs," and also about "some other plants which I had found in a coulee out at the buffalo drive site" (historic buffalo drive and hunting site, see Gilmore 1924b) north from here. One plant he learned about was *Mentha canadensis*, which "was said to be used as a common beverage as tea, and also as a medicine for colds generally, and especially for colds in the chest, also as a carminative [to relieve gas]." And in October 1926, Mrs. Mary

Figure 128. The leaves and flowers of wild mint, *Mentha arvensis* were used as a tea and also as a medicince to reduce the fever of children. Michael Haddock. Used with permission.

McCauley told him that they used the native mint as a condiment "for flavor and for drink". Gilmore collected the leaves used for tea and made a specimen of them which is archived in the Smithsonian Institution collections, NMAI #122981.

According to Ella Waters (rec. ca. 1979), "wild mint was drunk by children when they had a fever to reduce it. It was also used for horse medicine when a horse is sweeneyed, i.e. when the flesh come loose from its body at the joints" (Parks 1970–1997).

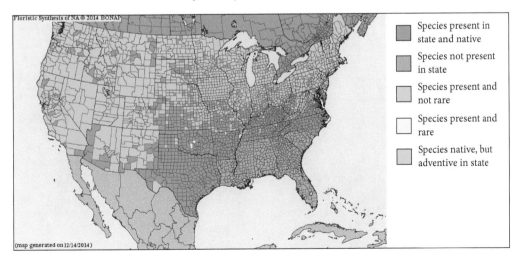

Figure 129. Map of U.S. counties with *Mentha arvensis* collections.

Mentzelia decapetala (Pursh) Urban and Gilg. Ex Gilg.

- **Tenpetal blazing star**
- *naRAhkaaxIštaakaáNU*, lit. "white flower"

Figure 130. The ten-petal blazing star, *Mentzelia decapetala*, had interesting uses as a pattern and also for painting. Michael Haddock. Used with permission.

The Arikara name is a participle that translates simply as "white flower", or "the flower that is white": *na-…-U* "participle" + *NAhkaaxíš-u'* "flower" + *-taakaan* "white".

The flower was used as decorative patterns in porcupine quill designs. Also, the fine, hairy substance on the ovary after the flowers are gone was also used as a brush for applying the paint in decorative designs to be worked on clothing (G).

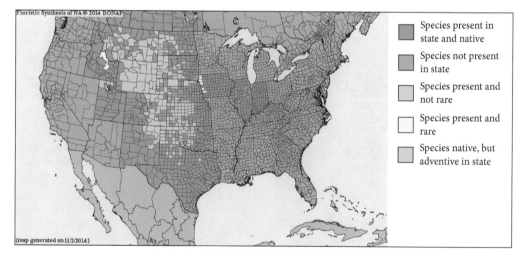

Figure 131. Map of U.S. counties with *Mentzelia decapetala* collections.

Monarda fistulosa L.

- **Beebalm** or **Horse mint, Wild Bergamot**
- *kAhahtAtpAxIsaá'u', kAhahpAsá'u', kAhahtAtWAsá'u'*
- *ItkAhahpAsá'u'*, lit. "ear bump"
- *kAhahtAtwaarúxti'*, lit. "holy fragrant plant"
- *ItkAhahwaarúxti'*, lit. "holy ear"
- *atIhneekAsaánu'*, lit. "ghost bean"

Figure 132. Beebalm, *Monarda fistulosa*, was noted for its sweet smell, and a medicinal tea was made to treat rheumatism and to alleviate the chills. Photograph by Craig Freeman. Used with permission.

Arikara speakers in the late twentieth century presented two variants of the name that appears to be recorded in Gilmore's notes. The first, *kAhahtAtpAxIsaá'u'*, means "fragrant plant with a head on the end": *kahaan-* "scent" + *taát-u'* "plant, stalk" + *páx-u'* "head" + *-isaa* "on the end". The second variant, *kAhahpAsá'u'*, means "fragrant bump": *kahaan-* + *pasa* "bump". Gilmore's transcriptions appear to represent a pronunciation *kAhahtAtWAsá'u'*, a plausible form comprised of *kahaan-* + *taát-u'* + *pasa* "fragrant plant with a bump". The name *ItkAhahpAsá'u'*, which appears to mean "ear bump" (*ItkAhaán-u'* 'ear' + *-pasa*) was recorded from a speaker in 1987, but may simply result from a metathesis (flipping around) of *kAhah-tAt-*.

The other names associated with *Monarda fistulosa* are: *kAhahtAtwaarúxti'* (*kahaan-* "scent" + *taát-u'* "plant" + *waaruxtii* "holy"), a name also applied to *Agastache foeniculum* (see above); *ItkAhahwaarúxti'*, which appears to mean "holy ear", recorded from the same speaker as *ItkAhahpAsá'u'*, and may derive from the same kind of metathesis; and, *atIhneekAsaánu'* (*átit* "bean" + *neekAsaán-u'* "ghost, spirit").

> There are two forms of *Monarda* both of which White botanists call *Monarda fistulosa*. They are, however, distinguished by Indian botanists as two different species and used for different purposes and have two different names. As specifically differentiated by the Indians, one species is a robust plant and has a strong-smelling odor, and the other is more delicate in structure and also the whole plant is very fragrant. Sweet smelling. These distinctions hold true in my own observation. The one here considered is the fragrant one, and its leaves were used for tea and also to perfume clothing, and especially as a perfume for pomade for the hair (G).

Gilmore collected this material and it is archived at the Smithsonian Institution, NMAI #126178. Horse mint was also used by the Arikara medicinally, "as an application for rheumatism, and taken internally for chills" (G). Parks (1970–1997) additionally records from an unidentified Arikara speaker that, "the flower petals of this plant were put in the mouth to relieve a sore throat."

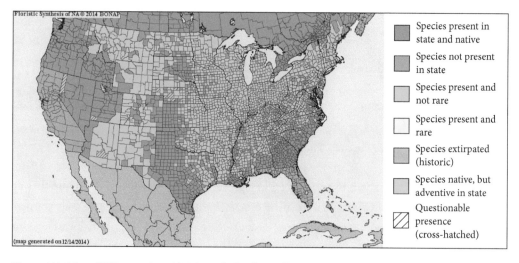

Figure 133. Map of U.S. counties with *Monarda fistulosa* collections.

Nicotiana quadrivalvis Pursh.

- **Indian tobacco** or **Arikara tobacco**
- *saakawíʼuʼ*

Figure 134. Indian tobaccao, *Nicotiana quadrivalvis,* was cultivated since ancient times and was used as a ceremonial smoking medicine. Photograph by Steven Norris. Used with permission.

This is the species of tobacco (Gilmore 1929) which has been cultivated by the Arikara since ancient time till the present (Gilmore 1922). It is not now used for common smoking, but only for ceremonies. It is used in all ceremonial smoking. When an old man dies some of it is placed in his coffin. When a person is sick this tobacco is burned on coals as an incense to all dead relatives of the sick person and to all the elements of the universe as a prayer that the disease may be removed and the person may recover. This Indian tobacco (*N. quadrivalvis*) is only native to California and adjacent states and was introduced from the West or Southwest a long time ago. The term for other types of tobacco is *naaWIškaánuʼ* or *hahnaaWIškaánuʼ*, literally "consumable smoke (wood)".

Gilmore and his seedsman friend, George F. Will Sr., took great interest in this plant and Gilmore made sure that a seed packet was archived. It is now in the Smithsonian Institution collections, NMAI #120028, along with a sample of ground leaves for smoking, NMAI #126322. The elder Crow Ghost stated that "this tobacco has no poison in it; will not hurt the smoker as the 'White man's tobacco' does" (G). Gilmore (1929) also retold the Arikara account of the Origin of Tobacco and Catching Eagles:

> A man reportedly fasted for several years and still received no blessing. At last, while he was fasting, a bird appeared to him and said: 'All our tribes (different species of birds) have been pleased by your persistence and strong will in fasting, so I have been sent here to show you our favor and give you

a gift.' This bird was an eagle. It had a branch of a plant in its beak when it sat down by the man. It was a branch of this tobacco. The eagle said: 'This plant is for you to smoke and make smoke offerings. The buds are to be your smoking materials. Also you see here the seeds. You will plant them and it will increase and you shall always have tobacco. This tobacco is one of the necessary things for the Mother Corn ceremonies. The principal Mother Corn ceremonies, agricultural ceremonies, in spring the prayers for blessing of the fields, for good crops, 2nd: in summer, in July or August continuing prayers for good weather and for pests and storms to be kept away; 3rd: the thanksgiving for the crop (in October and November). At this time gifts of food products, fruits, roots, corn, squash, sunflower seeds, etc., are brought as thank offerings into the temple. After the close of the ceremony these gifts are distributed to the poor and needy. This tobacco is also to be used in the 'Medicine Ceremonies' in the summer at the time the squash begins to set fruit. This tobacco is also to be used for the ceremony of *piireškáni'* [the Calumet ceremony, lit. 'Many-Hands Child', cf. Parks (2001: 379)].

'And I,' the eagle said, 'will be one of the main things offered. Whenever you make an undertaking you should wear one of these feathers (tail feathers of which there are 12), one of the two middle feathers, and we will be on the lookout and recognize this and will favor you in your undertaking, and give you success.' The eagle told the man he should go to a high place where the birds frequent. There, on the summit dig a pit in which he could hide, sitting with his head just even with the surface of the ground. 'You shall take a sweat bath and go to your eagle pit fasting and without food or drink all day.' He describes the making of the pit, carrying away the earth, making a frame and concealing it and fastening the bait, all with sinew. 'Thus you shall succeed in catching many eagles.' Then the man gave his gift to others.

When the eagle was seized a bunch of *Artemisia* was grasped and thrust toward the eagle and he would wrap it with his beak so he was incapacitated from injuring the man with his beak. Then the man would wrench the eagle's neck. The man would carry his prizes to his camp in the evening. There he could eat, drink, smoke and rest. Then before daylight take another sweat bath, change his clothes for others not used the day before, and go again fasting to his eagle pit for another day. After a siege of about 15 days of this, in months of October and November they came home with their feathers and give a thank offering as a part of the autumn Mother

Corn ceremony. He puts his store of plumes down before the alter as a gift to Mother Corn. They are distributed there in the general distribution (G).

Ella Waters (rec. ca. 1979) recounted that

> native tobacco was grown and tended by men, not women. It was used exclusively for 'medicine affairs.' The layer under the petals of the flowers was used: it was added to kinnikinnick [*uuxapáhAt, Cornus sericea* L.]. If one had no kinnikinnick, *napíhtu'* [*Rhus glabra* L.] was substituted. It was mixed with tobacco bought at the store—such as TB [an early twentiety century brand name no longer made] or Prince Albert—but kinnikinnick was preferred. A tobacco offering was made whenever one dug any kind of medicine root. A mixture of store tobacco, kinnikinnick, and Native tobacco was left (Parks 1970–1997).

Merriwether Lewis in 1804 believed that the Arikara had two species of tobacco, the larger one, *N. quadrivalvis*, as reported here, but also a smaller one, most likely *N. rustica*. He stated, "The recarres cultivate two species of tobacco, for the purpose of smoking in which way they use it altogether as they neither snuff nor chew—" (Lewis et al. 2002).

Lewis collected seeds from both species, and also a voucher specimen of the *N. quadrivalvis*, but he had only a detailed description of smaller species, which leads to the inference of it being *N. rustica*.

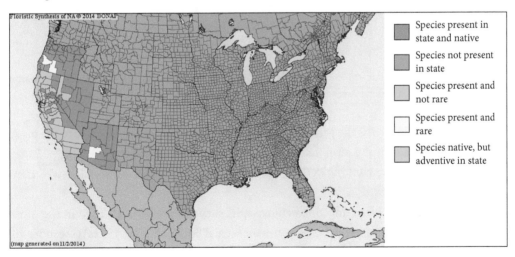

Figure 135. Map of U.S. counties with *Nicotiana quadrivalvis* collections.

Opuntia polyacantha Haw.

- **Plains prickly pear**
- *na'a átu'*
- *na'atkatóx*
- *na'atčíRUt*, in reference to the fruit

Figure 136. The dried, flat, de-spined pads of Plains prickly pear, *Opuntia polyacantha*, were used as part of the "Moon medicine," to relieve excessive menstrual flow. Photograph by Robyn Klein. Used with permission.

The term *na'aátu'* is used as the generic term for "cactus". More explicit reference to the prickly pear may be made by the term *na'atkatóx*, literally "flat cactus": *na'aát-u'* "cactus" + *katoox* "flat". The word for the fruit, *na'atčíRUt*, appears to mean "cactus lizard": *na'aát-u'* + *číRUt* "lizard".

The dried flat pads were singed to remove spines, cut and dried and "used in the Moon medicine, which was used to relieve excessive menstrual flow" (Gilmore 1931a) (see more discussion under chokecherry, *Prunus virginiana*). Specifically, Ella Waters (rec. ca. 1976/1977) describes that "the needles were burned and mixed with other roots to stop bleeding." Ella Waters (rec. ca. 1979) also states that the *na'atčíRUt* "was eaten" (Parks 1970–1997).

In mythological stories (Parks 1991a), someone being chased would often magically set patches of *na'aátu'* in the path of the dangerous pursuers. This would be accomplished by throwing a sharp-pointed object behind them, usually a comb (*piísus*)—in stories by Alfred Morsette (Parks 1991a:78, 114–119)—or in one case a knife (*neesítš*)—as told by Ella P. Waters (Parks 1991a:930). The cactus patch would spring from the ground where the item lands and slow down the villain. While this was likely a prickly pear (*Opuntia* species), it also could have been a pincushion cactus (*Escobaria* species).

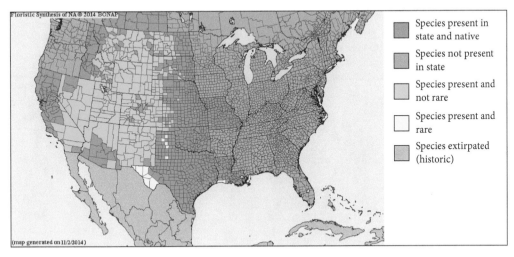

Figure 137. Map of U.S. counties with *Opuntia polyacantha* collections.

Parthenocissus vitacea (Knerr) Hitchc.

- **Woodbine or Virginia Creeper**
- *načiikuxtAhkoóku'u'*, lit. "gourd cover"

Figure 138. The seeds of Virginia creeper, *Pathenocissus vitacea,* were used as the noisemakers in rattles. Photograph by Katy Chayka. Used with permission.

The Arikara name appears to be composed of *načiikúx-tš* "gourd" + *-ran* "PL" + *kooku-u'* "covering".

Gilmore identifies this vine on separate occasions as Virginia creeper and honeysuckle (*Lonicera dioica*). The seeds from this plant are used as the noisemakers in rattles. Rattles were often made from dried gourds.

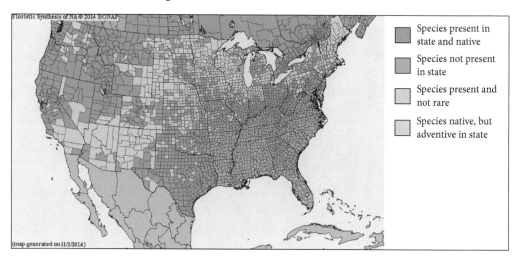

Figure 139. Map of U.S. counties with *Pathenocissus vitacea* collections.

Pediomelum argophyllum (Pursh) J. Grimes

- called *Psoralidium argophyllum* by Gilmore
- **Silverleaf scurfpea**
- *AxčiškátA*

Figure 140. A medicinal tea was made of silver-leafed scurfpea (*Pediomelum argophyllum*) leaves, tops, and roots to treat headache, or other swellings. Photograph by Craig Freeman. Used with permission.

The Arikara name seems to translate most literally as "against the foot bone", a meaning of obscure origin. Gilmore suggests that the name is used because the plants occur along the banks of a trail, i.e., a foot path.

When interviewed by Gilmore in July 1926, Albert Simpson said that "a tea was made from leaves and tops and roots of this plant, ground together and used for headaches. Also used to give a patient who has persistent hallucinations of unhealthy dreaming of seeing and talking with persons who are deceased."

Ella Waters (rec. ca. 1979) also says that "the root was used as medicine for treating swelling. It was dried and then ground up or pounded into a powder, which was rubbed on the afflicted area" (Parks 1970–1997).

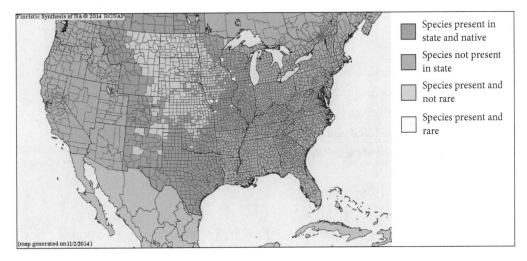

Figure 141. Map of U.S. counties with *Pediomelum argophyllum* collections.

Pediomelum esculentum (Pursh) Rydb.

- called *Psoralea esculenta* by Gilmore
- **Tipsin**, **Prairie turnip** or **large Indian breadroot, Breadroot Scurfpea**
- *WAsuúka'*

Figure 142. The roots of tipsin or prairie turnips, *Pediomelum esculentum,* were a very important wild food, cooked or roasted and eaten when fresh, or dried and ground up fine and then boiled into mush. Photograph by Craig Freeman. Used with permission.

Tipsin, or the prairie turnip, was one of the most important wild foods gathered by tribes across the Great Plains (Gilmore 1977). SteštAhkáta said,

> The commodity of which we got most from the Lakotas was dried tipsin roots. Tipsin grows abundantly in our country, but our women feared the Lakotas too much to go out on the prairie far from the villages to gather it. The Lakotas made strings of it of standard length. The length of a tipsin string was one arm-reach. They also split and dried the roots loose. We traded one *Axku-naaNIsaátu'* 'measuring basket' of shelled corn for four strings of tipsin roots, plus one *AxkunaaNIsaátu'* of dried split roots of tipsin (Gilmore 1926a).

She also stated:

> the most common unit of measure of commodities was the *AxkunaaN-Isaátu'*. The *AxkunaaNIsaátu'* was the measure of content of the common burden basket, which held about a bushel. One *AxkunaaNIsaátu'* of shelled corn was considered equal in value to one ordinary good buffalo robe or two packs of dried meat (Gilmore 1926a).

Ella Waters (rec. ca. 1979) commented that

> the prairie turnip was peeled and the outer parts used but not the tough inner part or core. Fresh turnips were boiled with the skin on, then eaten. They were thrown on coals, cooked; then peeled and eaten. The core wasn't eaten and was thrown away. Dried turnips were ground up fine and then boiled into mush (Parks 1970–1997).

Earlier trade accounts also indicate the importance of these roots and their flour. An expedition party, including Henry Brackenridge, who was accompanying Manual Lisa and his Missouri Fur Company's expedition, and who were also joined by John Bradbury, a Scottish botanist, had all traveled up the Missouri River from St. Louis and visited an Arikara village. On June 14, 1811, Brackenridge reported:

> Mr. Bradbury and I, took a walk into the upper village, which is separated from the lower by a stream about twenty yards wide. Entered several lodges, the people of which received us with kindness, placed mats and skins for us to sit on, and after smoking the pipe, offered us something to eat; this consisted of fresh buffaloe meat served in a wooden dish. They had a variety of earthen vessels, in which they prepared their food, or kept water. After the

meat, they offered us homony made of corn dried in the milk, mixed with beans, which was prepared with buffaloe marrow, and tasted extremely well; also pounded and made into gruel. The prairie turnip, is a root very common in the prairies, with something of the taste of the turnip but more dry; this they eat dried and pounded, made into gruel (Brackenridge 1814).

Also the trader Tabeau who lived with the Arikara in the early nineteenth century, discussed the importance to the flour from prairie turnips that could be traded:

> The Caninanbiches [Arapaho], Chayennes [sic] and others, who independently of their chargers, have many horses not laden, are rarely without this flour and, during the visit they paid to the Ricaras [Arikaras], they bartered it for maize at a profit of three or four measure for one (Abel 1939) .

The practice of women digging for tipsin is illustrated as a routine activity in the story of Star Husband and the Old Woman's Grandson—two versions of which are presented in Parks (1991a), as narrated by Ella P. Waters (Parks 1991a:889–922) and Dan Howling Wolf (Parks 1991a:1029–1044), respectively. A woman is abducted by a star (*sákaa'A*) and taken to a land in the sky to marry. Sometime later, she goes to dig up *WAsuúka'*, but her Star husband advises her to only dig turnips from high ground, never from lowlands or depressions. Curiosity gets the better of her, however, and when she digs up some *WAsuúka'* from the lowlands, she sees her homeland on the earth below her. She decides to return home with her child and she descends from the hole using a cord made for her by Old Woman Spider (*SuxtiikIsíš*). The Star Husband kills the woman on her way down the cord, but the son is spared and goes on to have several adventures, blessed by his celestial father.

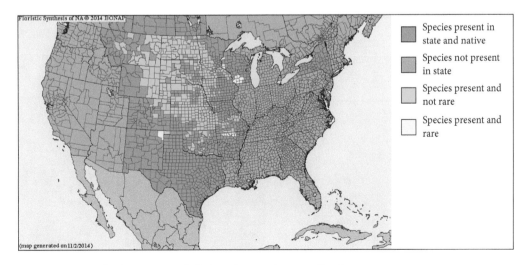

Figure 143. Map of U.S. counties with *Pediomelum esculentum* collections.

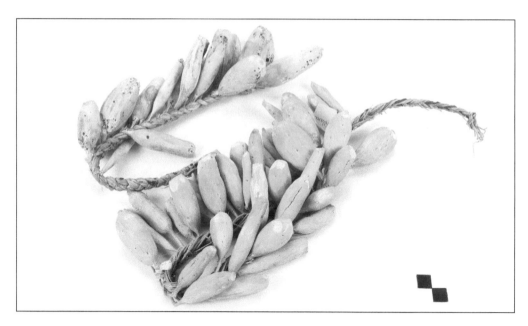

Figure 144. The prairie turnip or tipsin (the Lakota name that Gilmore encouraged us to adopt), was perhaps the most important wild food that was gathered by Arikara women, and women in tribes across the Great Plains. These braided strings of peeled roots show the thick swollen portion that was used as food—boiled or roasted, whole or ground, in sauce, soups, or stew. This string was purchased by Melvin Gilmore in 1923 from Mrs. Redtail. National Museum of the American Indian, Smithsonian Institution, Catalog Number 12/2999.

Phragmites australis (Cav.) Trin. Ex Steud.

- called *P. communis* by Gilmore
- **Common reed, Reed grass,** or **Cane grass**
- *paataátu'*

Figure 145. The hollow stems of common reed, *Phragmites australis,* were cut up into short pieces to made white, green or red beads for both children and adults. Photograph by Craig Freeman. Used with permission.

The Arikara term translates as "knee stalk": *paá-u'* "knee" + *taát-u'* "plant, stalk". See the entry for *Equisetum* above, which has a similar name in Arikara.

> The hollow culms or stems of *Phragmites* were used by children in play to make cylindrical beads by cutting them into short pieces and, some being green, others nearly white and still others red, they thus made variable-colored beads. They were also used by adults in the same manner to make decorative beads. This is one of the ancient forms of bead-making. In addition, the plant (not sure if it was leaves or the stem) was used by boys and girls to make a whistle (G).

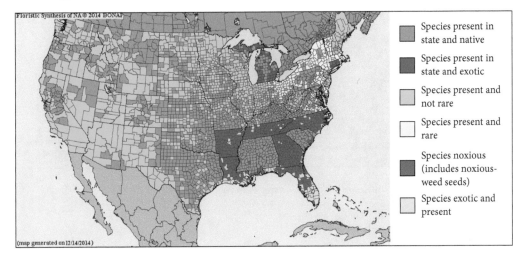

Figure 146. Map of U.S. counties with *Phragmites australis* collections.

Physalis heterophylla Nees.

- **Clammy ground cherry** or **Ground cherry, Wild tomatillos**

Figure 147. A green paper lantern of the clammy ground-cherry, *Physalis heterophylla*, will later in the fall have a ripe fruit. These fruits were gathered in quantity by Arikara children, mixed with clay, and eaten "with relish." Photograph by Michael Haddock. Used with permission.

SteštAhkáta told Gilmore in 1923

that in old times Arikara children gathered quantities of ground cherries and mixed them with a certain clay found near the Missouri River. They pressed and beat the mass of ground cherries and clay together into a jelly-like consistency. This preparation they then ate with relish.

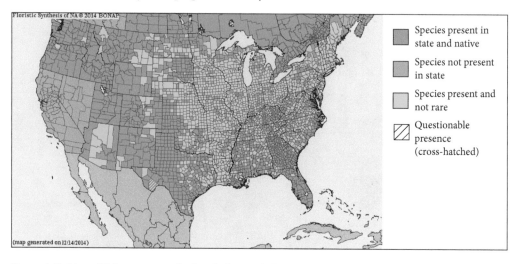

Species present in state and native

Species not present in state

Species present and not rare

Questionable presence (cross-hatched)

Figure 148. Map of U.S. counties with *Physalis heterophylla* collections.

Picea glauca (Moench) Voss

- called *P. canadensis* by Gilmore
- **White spruce**
- *načíšu' nakAhaanawíre, načíšu' nohkAhaanawireéRA*

Figure 149. White spruce, *Picea glauca*, was used as a perfume by both men and women, and it required travel by someone to get it as the closest locations are in the Black Hills and nearby mountains in western South Dakota. Photograph by Peter Dziuk. Used with permission.

The Arikara name is compounded from *način̆ū'*, the generic term for evergreen trees (pines, firs, and spruces), and *nakAhaanawíre*, meaning "fragrant wood": *rak- ~ haak-* "wood" + *kahaana-wi-* "scent" + *heer ~ reer* "good". The second variant, *način̆ū' nohkAhaanawireéRA*, simply means "fragrant evergreen".

The leaves are used for perfume by both men and women. Women bruised the leaves by slight chewing so that the aromatic odor was given off, then they would place these bruised leaves among their clothing. They would also perfume their hair with the bruised leaves, taking them in their hands and rubbing them through the hair. Men also used spruce leaves to perfume their bodies after the vapor bath, rubbing the bruised leaves all over themselves while still hot and moist from the bath.

> For the pleasant odor dry, brittle spruce gum was finely pulverized and the powder scattered among clothing. For adhesive purposes the gum was moistened and warmed and applied especially for attaching eagle downs or tufts of horsehair to the tips of eagle plumes (G).

In its aromatic usage, Ella Waters (rec. ca. 1979) added that "the leaves were also used for a smudge" (Parks 1970–1997).

The closest location of this species is the Black Hills and in the far northwest portion in South Dakota, but it is not in North Dakota. Thus, it was necessary to travel quite a distance to find this plant, or the Arikara had to trade for it.

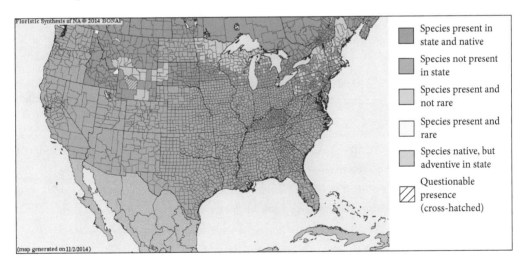

Figure 150. Map of U.S. counties with *Picea glauca* collections.

Pinus ponderosa Lawson & C. Lawson

- **Western yellow pine**, **Bull pine**, or **Ponderosa pine**
- *načíšu'*, also the generic term for pines, spruces, and firs
- *načiísu'*, in reference to tree resin or sap
- *načíšu' nakaraáku'*, in reference to the pine needles
- *načíšu' kaanipiíku'*, in reference to the pine cone

Figure 151. Ponderosa pine (*Pinus ponderosa*) needles were used for incense. Also in a case of serious illness pine needles would be burned every morning to drive away evil and to deodorize the house. Photograph by Kelly Kindscher.

Pine leaves, called in the Arikara language, *nakaraák-u'*—a term also used for tea leaves and tea itself—were used for incense. In a house where there was a case of serious illness pine leaves would be burned every morning as an incense to drive away evil and to deodorize the house. Also those who attended the sick would incense themselves with it, inhaling the smoke and incensing their hands and rubbing it over their bodies.

Pine resin when brittle was pulverized and the powder sprinkled among clothing for the pleasant odor. For an adhesive, resin was moistened and softened and applied, especially for such purposes as attaching eagle down or tufts of horsehair on tips of eagle plumes (G).

Ella Waters (rec. ca. 1979) stated that the "sap from evergreens was chewed like gum. It was also used to glue feathers on a war bonnet" (Parks 1970–1997).

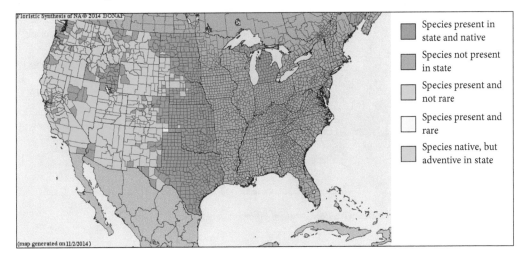

Figure 152. Map of U.S. counties with *Pinus ponderosa* collections.

Polygonatum biflorum (Walter) Elliott

- **Solomon's seal**

Figure 153. The seeds of solomon's seal, *Polygonatum biflorum,* were also used as the noisemakers in rattles. Photograph by Michael Haddock. Used with permission.

According to SteštAhkáta, the "seeds were used in rattles" (G).

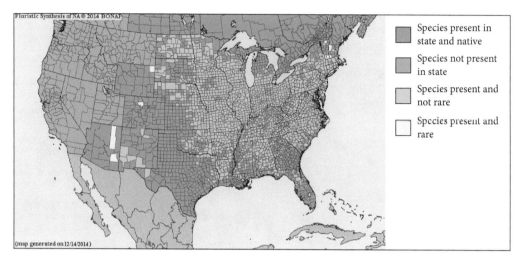

Figure 154. Map of U.S. counties with *Polygonatum biflorum* collections.

Polygonum sp.

- **Smartweed** or **Knotweed**
- *čipáts̆*

Figure 155. A leaf of knotweed, *Polygonum aviculare*, was used by children as a whistle. This plant was found along a trail. Photograph by Kelly Kindscher.

"A whistle was made by children from a leaf of this plant by placing a tip of the leaf on the tongue and suction was applied" (G).

Gilmore includes a note with knotweed, labeling it "dooryard grass." This may refer to the fact that the species often occurs in areas of moist, packed earth, such as along trails and in the dooryards of earth lodges.

Figure 156. Map of U.S. counties with *Polygonum* species collections.

Populus deltoides W. Bartram ex Marshall

- **Cottonwood**
- *WAxakúsu'*

Figure 157. The leaves, young branches, and dangling catkins of cottonwood (*Populus deltoides*), were used to feed horses. Photograph by Craig Freeman. Used with permission.

The Arikara name can be translated as "big *Populus*", the augmentative suffix *-kusu'*, denoting largesse, added to the stem *WAxaak-*. A young cottonwood may be referred to as *WAxačipiriínu'*: *WAxaák-u'* "cottonwood" + *čipiriin* "new, young".

Gilmore interviewed White Bear about the rearing and caring for horses in July 1923. In the winter the horses were fed some corn.

> They were also fed twigs and bark [*haakIskuúxu'*] of young cottonwood. In the evenings the people would be sitting round the fireplace chatting and telling stories while they peeled cottonwood branches and threw the bark back to the horses.

Ella Waters (rec. ca. 1979) also stated that

> logs about four feet long were placed in the horse corral in the earthlodge during the winter. The horses ate the green bark [*skataátu'*]. After they ate off the bark, the log was used for firewood [*naakAhíšu'*]. Logs were also used as foundation posts [*saakunaakaawí'u'*] and beams [*NAhaakIsa'iítu'*] in earthlodges.

She adds (rec. 1975) that the (green) inner bark was "used for tying bundles or baskets" (Parks 1970–1997).

Ella Waters further points out medicinal concoctions from parts of the cottonwood. "The catkins (*kaanipiíku'*) of young cottonwood trees were used by men in making love medicine" (rec. ca. 1979) while "the soft white substance in cottonwood logs [*haakItkaataáatš*] floats down the Missouri River and is used for medicine" (rec. 1976), although that medicine is unidentified (Parks 1970–1997).

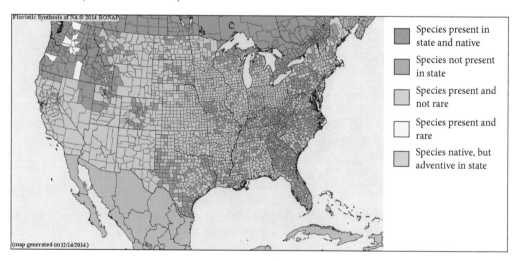

Figure 158. Map of U.S. counties with *Populus deltoides* collections.

Prunus americana Marshall

- **American plum** or **Wild plum**
- *niWAharít*, generically or referring to the fruit
- *niWAhaRIhnaáku'*, in specific reference to the tree

Figure 159. The red ripe fruits of the wild plum, *Prunus americana*, were eaten fresh or dried. Also the perfect timing of fruit ripening was known, as it was the time when the seeds could be removed easily from the flesh. Photograph by Kelly Kindscher.

Plums were eaten fresh and dried for winter. According to SteštAhkáta: "We know the right time to seed them," before they are soft ripe, when they become more difficult to easily remove them. Dried plums are pounded up in winter and cooked. Gilmore purchased dried plums from Mrs. Redtail on the Fort Berthold Reservation in August 1923 and these are now in the Smithsonian Institution archives.

Also, the Arikara observed that "when the wild plum blossoms were evident in the spring, it was time to plant squash and beans." Dried plums are part of the Smithsonian Institution collections, NMAI #123036.000.

In the story of how an evil man would demand impossible tasks of his daughter's suitors, as told by Alfred Morsette (Parks 1991a:228–232, and see the entry for *Amelanchier* above), one of the tasks set before the protagonist is to retrieve *niWAharít* during the winter, when none grow. With the aid of a magical old woman who lives in the woods, the young man is able to conjure plums from a branch by shaking it over the smokehole of the old woman's earthlodge. The *niWAharít* fall from the branch and the young man is able to take the load back to his evil father-in-law, who simply desires them for a snack. This request by the father-in-law reinforces his villainy in its blatant disregard for the regular Arikara association of the wild plum with seasonal change, as described above. Such stories may have implicitly helped to teach children about this seasonal association. Offhandedly, the relish the father-in-law shows for the plums also demonstrates the delectability of *niWAharít* for the Arikara.

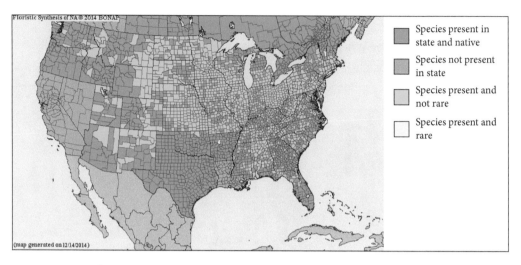

Figure 160. Map of U.S. counties with *Prunus americana* collections.

Prunus pumila L.

- called *P. besseyi* by Gilmore
- **Sandcherry**, **Nebraska sand cherry**, or **Bessey's cherry**
- *kUxapaánu'*

Figure 161. Harvested sand cherries, *Prunus pumila,* were used to make a sauce, and sand cherry juice was mixed with corn meal to make a tasty corn pudding. Photograph by Peter Dziuk. Used with permission.

"The Arikara name, *kUxapaánu'*, means 'sitting-hiding': *-kux* 'be sitting' + *-apaan* 'hidden'" (G). There is a belief concerning the sand cherry among several Plains tribes (Gilmore 1977), that one must approach it from the lee side when gathering it, for if one comes from the windward side the cherries will be bitter to the taste.

> The Arikara say that in ancient time this was one of the principal food fruits used by their people. It is a low-growing shrub, a dwarf cherry tree only a few inches tall, or at most a foot and a half or two feet high, but profusely bearing large-sized purple-black cherries which are of good flavor. The sand cherry was abundant in the Sand Hills region of north-central Nebraska, which was a part of the realm of the Arikara nation about four or five centuries ago. It also occurs to some extent in sandy places in North Dakota.

> The Arikara made sauce of sand cherries. They also mixed sand cherry juice with corn meal to make a corn pudding. Corn pudding was also made by mixing into the corn meal the whole of sand cherries, pits and all pounded to a pulp. Sometimes the broken fragments of seedpit shells were strained out in a basket strained before mixing the cherry pulp with the corn meal to make the pudding (G).

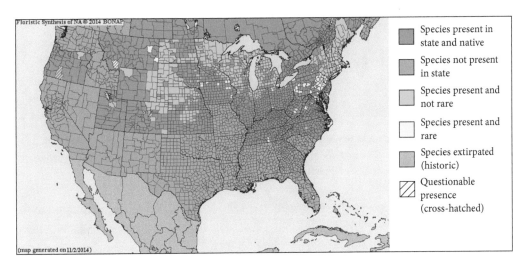

Figure 162. Map of U.S. counties with *Prunus pumila* collections.

Prunus virginiana L.

- **Chokecherry**
- *nakaánus*, generically or in reference to the fruit
- *nakaaNUstaáku'* or *nakaaNUstaátu'*, in explicit reference to the tree
- *nakaaNUsčiísu'*, in reference to chokecherry resin
- *nakaaNUstakeešíšu', nakaaNUstakeéšUx* refer to a chokecherry patty
- *nakaánus huú'u'* refers to chokecherry pudding

Figure 163. Chokecherry, *Prunus virginiana,* fruits were abundant and were used fresh or dried with many foods. Often the cherries were dried and finely pounded up later (fruit and pit together, to make flavorful dishes of food. Photograph by Kelly Kindscher.

When referring specifically to the plant itself, the Arikara would use either the compound *nakaaNUstaáku'* "chokecherry tree" (*nakaánus* + *rak- ~ haak-* "wood, tree") or *nakaaNUstaátu'* "chokecherry plant" (*nakaánus* + *taát-u'* "plant, stem"). This variation probably depends on whether the speaker is construing the plant as a tree or as a smaller bush.

In the publication that Gilmore wrote called "Arikara Commerce" (1926a), he stated:

> The Arikaras obtained dried chokecherries from the Lakotas, although they also put up some for themselves. When they bought them from the Lakotas they paid one *AxkunaaNIsaátu'* (or large basket) of shelled corn for one-half *AxkunaaNIsaátu'* of dried chokecherries.

More discussion of this commerce is described under the prairie turnip, *Pediomelum esculentum*. When compared to juneberries (*naakunaánu'*), another fruit gathered and traded as food, it was stated: "The chokecherries are easier to gather, but the process of pounding to a pulp and drying is laborious, hence they were equalized in price."

Chokecherries were a favorite flavoring for corn mush, also called chokecherry-corn pudding (*nakaánus huú'u'*), as Gilmore wrote about them in "Some Interesting Indian Foods" (Gilmore 1926c), either using chokecherry fruits

> with pits crushed or with pits strained out by means of a basket colander. Another variety of mush, *hoonaáxu'*, literally 'cooked mush', was made entirely from meal of parched corn. For this dish flint corn was parched and then ground in a mortar. The resulting meal was then made into mush by boiling in the usual way by gradually dropping and stirring into boiling water. This mush was then served either plain or seasoned with suet, or with dried chokecherries mixed in during the cooking process. The chokecherries were gathered when ripe and pounded to a pulpy mass, pits and all, shaped into cakes [*nakaaNUstakeešíšu'* or *nakaaNUstakeéšUx*, both simply meaning 'pounded chokecherry'] and dried in the sun. Thus preserved, they were ready for use at all times in various preparations. For flavoring the mush, the cakes of dried cherries were broken up and stirred into the meal.

> The moon medicine *nakaaNUsčiísu'*, 'chokecherry juice', was used to cure a woman having too great a menstrual flow. It was from the gummy exudate of chokecherry sap, the root of *paatAhuunuukaásu'* 'scarlet globe mallow (*Sphaeralcea coccinea*)', *na'atkatóx* 'prickly pear cactus (*Opuntia polyacantha*)' that has been singed, peeled and dried, and the root of *čiriNAsiínu'* 'cattail (*Typha latifolia*)'. These were all dried, pounded, [and] mixed dry. When administered, put two pinches in a cup mixed with hot water. Given to drink until relieved. And in case of postpartum hemorrhage the juice of the chokecherry is given to the patient to drink. Also in such cases the gum which exudes from the chokecherry tree (*Prunus virginiana*) is triturated [finely ground] together with the root of scarlet globemallow (*Sphaeralcea coccinea*) and made into an infusion which is given as a drink (Gilmore 1931a).

Also, Ella Waters (rec. 1976) commented that *nakaaNUsčiísu'*, chokecherry resin, "was mixed with other roots and used to treat diarrhea." She adds (rec. 1973) that "the outer bark of the tree was scraped downward and outward with a sharp cutting instrument. The shavings were used for making tea" (Parks 1970–1997).

Gilmore purchased a traditional cherry pounder *(kaNIstakeéšišUx)* from Mrs. Redtail in 1923, a big cherry maul NMAI # 122996, and flattened chokecherry cakes NMAI # 122987 and they are part of the Smithsonian Institution collections.

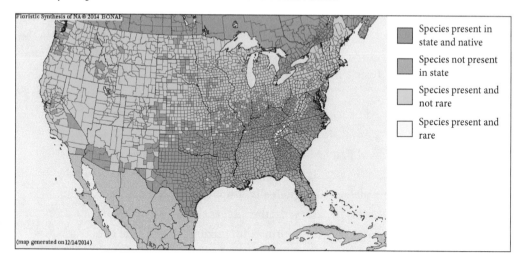

Figure 164. Map of U.S. counties with *Prunus virginiana* collections.

Figure 165. Another Cherry Hammer/pounder, used to crush dried chokecherries, pits and all, for use in corn mush, or into a fine powder that was reconstituted as a tasty, fruit sauce. This tool was purchased by Melvin Gilmore in 1923 from Mrs. Redtail. National Museum of the American Indian, Smithsonian Institution, Catalog Number 12/2953.

Psoralidium tenuiflorum (Pursh) Rydb.

- called *Psoralea floribunda* by Gilmore
- **Slimflower scurfpea or wild alfalfa**
- *AxčiškátA*

Figure 166. The roots of slimflower scurfpea, *Psoralidium tenuiflorum,* were used as medicine to treat fever that a baby might have. Photograph by Craig Freeman. Used with permission.

Gilmore records the same Arikara name for Slimflower scurfpea as for Silverleaf scurfpea. It is found in similar habitat to the above *Psoralidium argophyllum.* The chemistry is different, so they likely were used differently as different species. The "roots are used as a medicine for babies, especially for fever" (G).

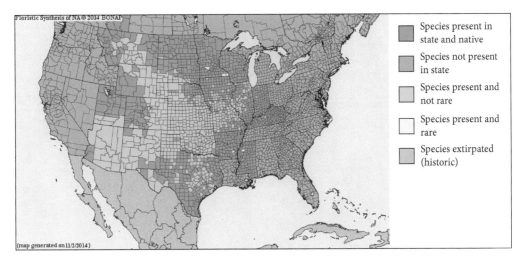

Figure 167. Map of U.S. counties with *Psoralidium tenuiflorum* collections.

Ratibida columnifera (Nutt.) Woot. & Standl.

- called *Lepachys columnaris* by Gilmore
- **Upright prairie coneflower** or **Yellow coneflower**
- *saakAxtItkú'u'*

Figure 168. The scented seeds of the yellow coneflower, *Ratibida columnifera*, were used to mask the human odor by scattering them over a sinew snare when it was set for catching small animals. Photograph by Kelly Kindscher.

"[The] Arikara name, *saakAxtItkú'u'*, means 'mouse-tail' [*saákAx* 'mouse' + *NItkú'u'* 'tail']. When a sinew snare was set for catching small animals, the seeds of this plant were scattered over it to mask the human odor" (G).

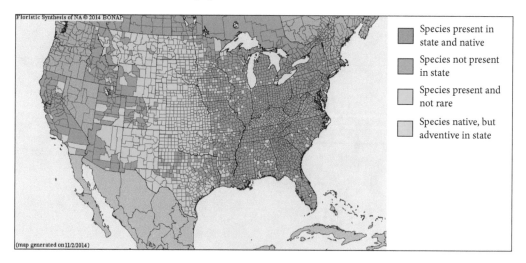

Figure 169. Map of U.S. counties with *Ratibida columnifera* collections.

Rhus glabra L.

- **Smooth sumac**
- *nipíhtu'*
- *napíhtu'*

Figure 170. The dried leaves of smooth sumac, *Rhus glabra,* were used as part of a smoking mix. Photograph by Craig Freeman. Used with permission

Ella Waters (rec. 1973, ca. 1979) describes that

> the dried leaves of this weed were mixed with kinnikinnick (*Arctostaphylos uva-ursi*) for making a tobacco, *nanoóxu'*. If one had no kinnikinnick, *napíhtu'* could be substituted, although kinnikinnick was preferred. It was also mixed with store-bought tobacco, e.g. TB [a brand that is no longer made] or Prince Albert (Parks 1970–1997).

Gilmore also stated that the fruits, or if not available, the root, were steeped and applied for rash or other eruptions. Young leaves were dried, powdered and used the same way.

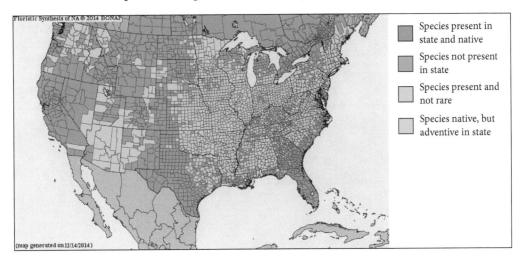

Figure 171. Map of U.S. counties with *Rhus glabra* collections.

Ribes spp.

- **Currants** and **Gooseberries**
- *huučíRIt*

Figure 172. The fruits of gooseberries and currants, this one is *Ribes aureum,* were eaten fresh, and likely not dried as they were never abundant enough. Photograph by Michael Haddock. Used with permission.

The Arikara name is also used for cactus fruits, perhaps due to the spines on both gooseberries and cactus fruits. According to Mrs. Butcher, "Gooseberries and wild currants were said to be used fresh, not dried for winter." Gilmore added that they were "probably never ... found in sufficient quantity." There are four species of both currants and gooseberries that are native to North Dakota.

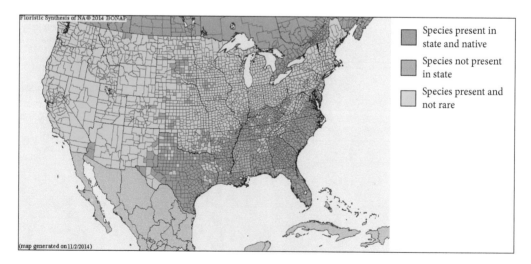

Figure 173. Map of U.S. counties with *Ribes* species collections.

Rosa arkansana Porter

- called *R. pratincola* by Gilmore
- **Prairie rose** or **Prairie wild rose**
- *páhAt*, in reference to the rose hip berry
- *pahAstaátu'*, in reference to the plant
- *pAhahnaanataaká*, in reference to the flower
- *nakAskoótu'*, in reference to the galls

Figure 174. The red rose hips, or fruits follow the vibrant pink flowers of wild praire rose, *Rosa arkansana*. These fruits were eaten for food, but the hairs inside them sometimes caused problems as told in a funny traditional Arikara story. Photograph by Craig Freeman. Used with permission.

The Sahnish name for the rose hip berry, *páhAt*, is also used to refer to tomatoes. The term is derived from the lexical root *pahaat* "red". Direct reference to the plant involves compounding the stem *taát-u'* "plant, stem". The name of the flower, *pAhahnaanataaká*, is based on the color, including the root words *pahaat* "red" and *taakaan* "white"—the name of the flower is also used in reference to the color "pink"—although the exact derivation from these roots is unclear. Galls were called *nakAskoótu'*, literally "rotten woody herb": *rak-* "wood" + *kás-u'* "root, herb" + *koot* "rot, die".

"Insect galls from the wild rose together with wild licorice root (*Glycyrrhiza lepidota*) *kAskatarí* were dried and comminuted [reduced to fine particles] by pounding, mixed, boiled, and strained to drink as a remedy for sore throat." Parks (1970–1997) records an unidentified Arikara speaker as saying that "the bark of the stems was peeled and used for treating eye problems."

Ella Waters (rec. ca. 1979) stated that "the *páhAt* berry was boiled and then strained to remove its seeds. This concoction was then thickened with cornstarch and eaten" (Parks 1970–1997).

While the fruits or hips are edible, as described, care must be taken to avoid eating the hairs inside, which can cause severe itching and irritation. A note of caution is illustrated in Lillian Brave's story of Coyote, Artichoke, and the Rose Hips (Parks 1991a:855–858). Coyote is beset by extreme flatulence after being convinced to eat Jerusalem artichokes. Eventually his rectum bursts. To further antagonize *sčiRIhtšutaRAháxu'*, Mischievous Coyote, a *pahAstaátu'* Wild Rose convinces him to eat the *páhAt*. The rose hips begin to heal his rectum, but then the seeds from the fruit cause him further anal irritation, and he drags his rectum on the ground until it bleeds, trying to ease the itching. The *tšuúxIt* and *páhAt* finally spare Coyote after he does a good deed for the *uuxapáhAt* Red Osier Dogwood saplings (see the entry for *Cornus sericea* above).

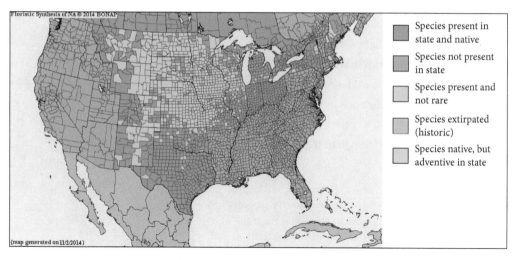

Figure 175. Map of U.S. counties with *Rosa arkansana* collections.

Rosa woodsii Lindl.

- **Woods' rose** or **Wild wood rose**
- *páhAt*, in reference to the rose hip
- *pahAstaátu'*, in explicit reference to the whole plant
- *pAhahnaanataaká*, in reference to the flower

Figure 176. The spiny outer bark of the wild wood rose, *Rosa woodsii,* was scraped off so that the inner bark could be used as a tasty tea. Photograph by Craig Freeman. Used with permission.

The same Arikara terms are used for the Woods' rose as for the Prairie rose, and these species were likely used interchangeably.

> The inner bark of the bushes of this tall spiny wild rose was used for a drink like tea. The spines and outer bark were scraped off or singed off, then the inner bark was stripped off and tied up in small bundles and dried. When desired for use, these bundles of bark were steeped in hot water to make a pleasant beverage (G).

Gilmore collected some of this material and it is part of the Smithsonian Institution collections, NMAI #122985.

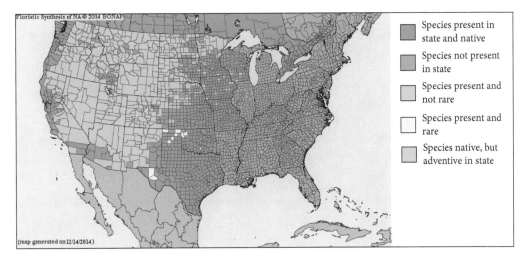

Figure 177. Map of U.S. counties with *Rosa woodsii* collections.

Rubus idaeus L. subsp. *strigosus* (Michx.) Focke

- **Wild raspberry** or **Gray-leaf red raspberry**
- *apáru'*

Figure 178. The wild raspberry, *Rubus idaeus,* fruit was used for food, and the leaves were used for tea. Photograph by Matt Lavin. Used with permission.

"The fruit was used for food, the leaves for tea" (G). The Arikara name is also used for wild strawberries (*Fragaria virginiana* Duchesne).

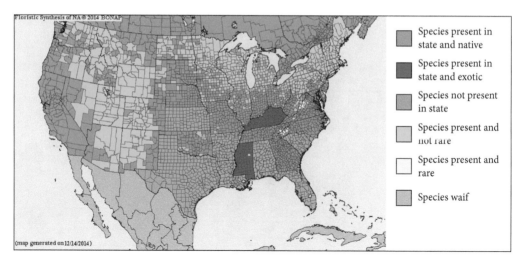

Figure 179. Map of U.S. counties with *Rubus idaeus* collections.

Salix spp.

- **Willow**
- *čitapátš*

There were several species of willow used by the Arikara, and there were specific uses for crack, diamond, and sandbar willow respectively, as discussed below. Willows as a group had many uses and some may have been used interchangeably, but the plant sophistication of the Arikara can be seen in the specific uses of these similar willow species below. Willows as a group were part of the material used in the roof structures of the earth lodges. The straight and strong willow stems, along with a layer of big bluestem grass bundles, were used to hold up as much as a foot or more of soil that was the final covering of their lodges, which were large and strong enough for people to sit on top of them.

Figure 180. Map of U.S. counties with *Salix* species collections.

Figure 181. SteštAhkáta "Yellow Corn Woman", also called Snow, making baskets with two children seated next to her, showing them how to take willow saplings and turn them into baskets. She was a midwife and basketmaker and artist, who was 83 when Melvin Gilmore interviewed her and took this picture at her house in 1923 on the Fort Berthold Reservation in North Dakota. National Museum of the American Indian, Smithsonian Institution, Catalog Number NO8708.

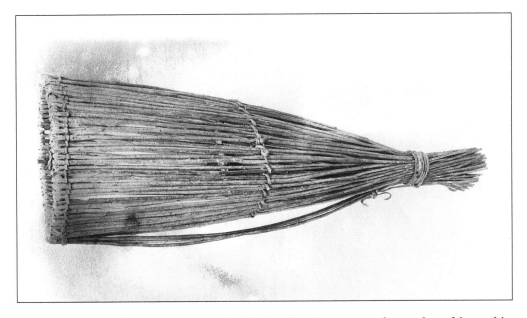

Figure 182. This is the dipping basket made of willow by White Bear to use in dipping the catfish out of the fish trip. Once the fish were in the trap, they needed to handled, and one did not want to get stung by the spines.

Salix amygdaloides Andersson

- Gilmore called it *S. nigra*, but that species name is not recognized as a North Dakota species today.
- **Peachleaf willow** or **Crack willow**
- *čitapAhnaáNUx*

Figure 183. The inner bark of peach-leafed willow, *Salix amygdaloides,* was used for basket-making. Photograph by Craig Freeman. Used with permission.

The Arikara name appears to translate as "hairy willow": *čitapát-tš* "willow" + *-raanux* "hairy".

This is the species whose inner bark was used for basket making. Gilmore had StcštΛhkáta make work baskets for him in 1923 and also interviewed her about how they were made.

> The baskets, *satwáhAt,* literally 'red basket' (*saát-ú'* 'basket' + *-wahat* 'red')—is usually made from crack willow bark alone and, without dying, the inner bark turns a dull reddish brown. In preparing strips of bark for plaiting, they are cut into long narrow strips like leather thongs. The width of these strips is less accordingly for the smaller, finer baskets (*satčiripásIt*), merely a convenient width in each case, no standard width as by fractions of an inch as with us. There were over 9 styles of willow baskets made, with combinations of colored and uncolored bark. Sometimes the bark of uncolored boxelder (*Acer negundo*) bark was used in patterns with the crack willow to obtain red and white baskets. Black bark could also be obtained soaking the willow bark in the black mud for 48 hours.

Gilmore provides a longer discussion of basket making in *Arikara Basketry* (Gilmore 1925b). Gilmore collected much of this material used for baskets, identified it to this species, and it is part of the Smithsonian Institution collections, NMAI #122956-957, 1223014-016.

William Deane Jr. (rec. ca. 1979) also affirmed this use, stating:

> the bark strips were put in the blue mud in a spring. They were left there for
> approximately two days, until black. Other bark from the same tree was put
> in water to soak, turning it white. Black and white strips were then used for
> weaving baskets (Parks 1970–1997).

Lillian Brave and Angela Plante (rec. 1987) added that "the wood was used in making drums"
(Parks 1970–1997).

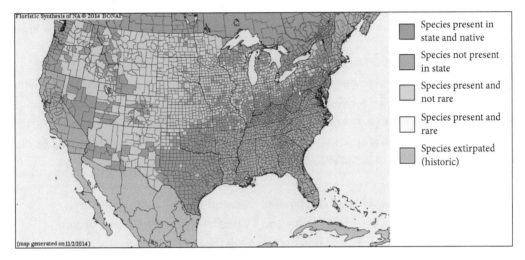

Figure 184. Map of U.S. counties with *Salix amygdaloides* collections.

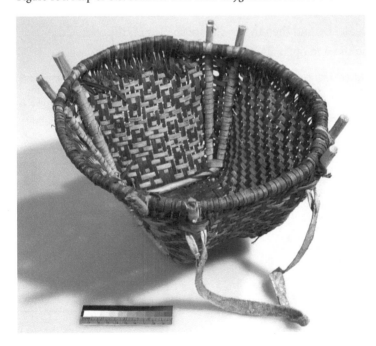

Figure 185. This small burden basket was made by SteštAhkáta for Melvin Gilmore in 1923. The darkened splints are peachleaf willow, as the inner bark dries a darkened red-brown, and the light splints are of box elder (*Acer negundo*). National Museum of the American Indian, Smithsonian Institution, Catalog Number 12/3014.

Salix eriocephala Michx.

- **Diamond Willow** or **Missouri River willow**

- *čitapAtkúsu'*

Figure 186. The diamond willow, *Salix eriocephala,* was the preferred wood for making the perfect hot fire for roasting corn. Photograph by Matt Lavin. Used with permission.

The Arikara name means "large willow": *čitapát-tš* "willow" + *-kusu'* "large".

Gilmore provided interesting details on Arikara cooking and wrote an article titled, "Some Interesting Indian Foods" for Good Health Magazine in 1926 where he stated: "In the country of the Arikara tribe on the upper Missouri River the diamond willow abounds. The dry wood of this species makes a quick, clean, hot fire, and it is most commonly used in that region as a fuel for cooking." For cooking green corn,

> the Arikara lay a bed of dry poles of diamond willow about ten or twelve feet in length. On this bed of dry, small wood a woman lays the ears of corn retaining their husks, and watches and tends them, deftly turning them with a pole until they are properly cooked. The ears when cooked, are tossed into a pile. There they lie steaming until they are sufficiently cool, when they are husked at convenience, and then the grains are shelled off the cobs and spread to dry in the sun and open air (Gilmore 1926c).

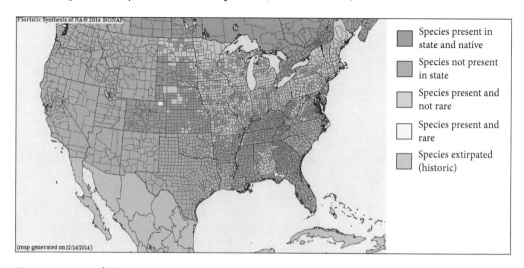

	Species present in state and native
	Species not present in state
	Species present and not rare
	Species present and rare
	Species extirpated (historic)

Figure 187. Map of U.S. counties with *Salix eriocephala* collections.

Figure 188. SteštAhkáta is dying willow splints in black mud in order to have a third color for making baskets. The black was in addition to the white of box elder and the red-brown willow bark. National Museum of the American Indian, Smithsonian Institution, Catalog Number NO8732.

Salix interior Rowlee

- **Sandbar willow**
- *čitapAtwáhAt, čitapAtWAhaátu', čitapAtpáhAt, čitapAtpAhaátu'*

Figure 189. The sandbar willow, *Salix interior,* had many uses, including it was the favorite wood to use in making fish traps. Photograph by Craig Freeman. Used with permission.

All of the variants of the Sandbar willow's Arikara name mean "red willow", the second and fourth forms simply adding the noun suffix *-u'*, and the four variants showing both pronunciations of the word meaning "red": *čitapát-tš* "willow" + *-wahat ~ -pahat* "red".

This was the species of willow that was used to construct fish traps (*čískA*), with 100 vertical stems used to make each panel that enclosed the trap. The bottom end of the stems were sharpened so that they would stick in the sand. The trap, about 10 feet in diameter was supported by four strong ash (or other species) posts and used to trap catfish (*čiwanaaNIšíšu'*) and other fish (*čiwáhtš*) from the Missouri River. Gilmore had one created so that he could write about it and take photos (Gilmore 1924a). The ingenious method of making the trap, baiting it with maggot-infested rotten meat (*tsaskoótu'*), locating it in the proper place in the river backwaters, and following ceremonial protocols, resulted in successful harvests of fish from the river from the time when corn ripe enough for roasting ears until the water got too uncomfortably cold for fishing in mid-August. After successfully trapping them, the fish were shared with members of the tribe. According to an elder, White Bear, whom Gilmore interviewed in 1923, "the bark of young sandbar willow was also used in the fish medicine that was used to treat catfish stings (finning) along with baneberry [*škanikaatít*]" (*Actea rubra*, see for more treatment details) (Gilmore 1924a).

Also this willow species, along with *haakakoótu'* buckbrush (*Symphoricarpos occidentalis*) were natural indicators of good soil. The Arikara specifically chose sandy soil with good humus, but areas that also contained these plants were indicators of the proper soil for their fields.

William Deane, Jr. (rec. ca. 1979) describes how

> a stick of sandbar willow, *kUxwaawaníkUx*, approximately 30 inches long, straight, was used by boys for a throw game. On one end, circular notches are added up about 6 inches, then come down with another circular notch. Several vertical notches are added (Parks 1970–1997).

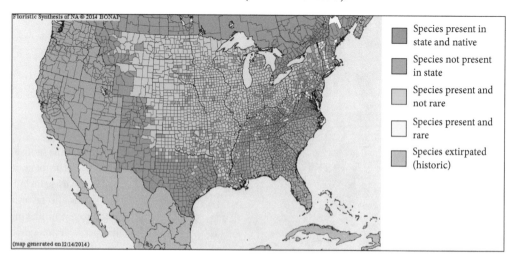

Figure 190. Map of U.S. counties with *Salix interior* collections.

Sanguinaria canadensis L.

- **Bloodroot**
- *kAswáhAt*, lit. "red root"

Figure 191. The roots of bloodroot, *Sanguinaria canadensis,* with their red sap, were used to stop bleeding. Photograph by Kelly Kindscher.

The Arikara name is composed of the oft-recurring terms *kás-u'* "root, herb" + *wahat* "red", in description of the salient coloration of the plant's root.

Ella Waters (rec. ca. 1979) describes the plant's preparation for medicinal application:

> the root is pounded into powder, which is then inserted into the nose to stop nasal hemorrhaging. Also, its roots were used alone to check hemorrhaging from the mouth or nose. The roots were dried and pounded into a powder, which was then sniffed (Parks 1970–1997).

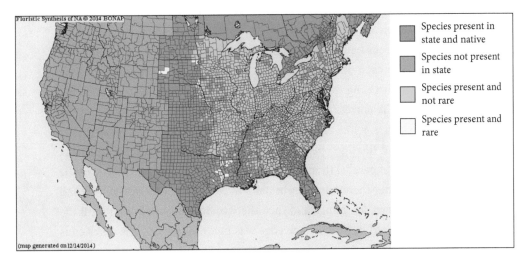

Figure 192. Map of U.S. counties with *Sanguinaria canadensis* collections.

Schoenoplectus tabernaemontani (C.C. Gmel.) Palla

- called *Scirpus validus* by Gilmore
- **Softstem bulrush** or **Bulrush**
- *híš*

Figure 193. The stems of softstem bulrush, *Schoenoplectus tabernaemontani,* were woven into mats. Photograph by Michael Haddock. Used with permission.

The culms of bulrush were used to form the weft in making mats (*hIštaátu'*) and bags (*kAxiíts*), the warp being rawhide thongs (*taRAhúhts*). These mats were made for household furnishing and also for use in the sacred lodge or tribal temple. In one form of mat, two lines of pegs were driven into the earth. These pegs being a few inches apart in line and the lines being at a distance from each other according to the length they desired to have the mat, a rawhide thong was attached to the end peg in one of these lines and stretched to the corresponding end peg of the other line, then around the second peg in this line and back to the second peg in the other line, and from it around the third peg and to the third peg in the second line, etc., until a figure of parallel thongs covered the space desired for the size of the mat to be made. Then bulrushes in pairs were alternatively woven over and under these parallel thongs and thus the weaving was continued until the pattern was filled in. The selvage edge was made by turning the outer ends of the bulrushes back over the outside thong.

Another form of mat was made by braiding in broad braids four, six or eight rushes together and these broad strips were then joined side by side by threading in another bulrush. Thus the joined, broad flat braids made a mat. Bulrushes also were woven into utility bags (G).

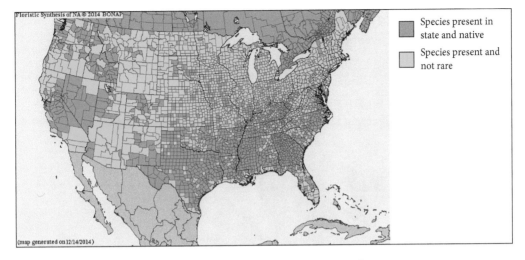

Figure 194. Map of U.S. counties with *Schoenoplectus tabernaemontani* collections.

Figure 195. Mrs. Sitting Bear, demonstrating the bulrush mat making process on the Fort Berthold Reservation in 1923. National Museum of the American Indian, Smithsonian Institution, Catalog Number NO8757.

Figure 196. This softstem bulrush mat was made by Mrs. Sitting Bear on the Fort Berthold Reservation in 1923. Mats were used in the home for a variety of purposes. National Museum of the American Indian, Smithsonian Institution, Catalog Number 12/2974.

Shepherdia argentea (Pursh) Nutt.

- **Buffaloberry** or **Silver buffaloberry, Bullberry**
- *naáni'Is*, generic or in referring to the fruit
- *naaNIsaáku'*, in explicit reference to the tree
- *naaNIsiNAhkáta*, lit. "yellow buffaloberry", in reference to plants with yellow fruit
- *huunaaní'Is* is bullberry pudding

Figure 197. The tasty, tart red fruits of buffaloberry, *Shepherdia argentea*, were eaten and also dried. Photograph by Matt Lavin. Used with permission.

As with other fruit-bearing trees, the basic term—*naaní'Is* here—is used of the fruit or in generic reference to the plant. Explicit reference to the tree itself involves compounding -*haak* "wood, tree" to that basic term, as in *naaNIsaáku'*. Berries that are yellow instead of the typical red, or by extension the plant that bears such berries, can be called *naaNIsiNAhkáta*, from *naaní'Is + rahkataan* "yellow".

Buffaloberries were another tasty fruit that were eaten by the Arikara. According to SteštAhkáta,

> buffalo berries were not an article of commerce with the Sioux. They were picked by knocking off into a basket (as the bushes are spiny). But by harvesting them with this method, leaves, twigs and other refuse were mixed with the harvested berries. So, then the basket was taken to water, immersed and stirred, refuse comes to the surface, floats off. Then the washed berries were now spread on a clean hide and another hide was spread over. On this upper hide the women trod until the berries were well pulped. The mashed berries were then shaped into cakes in a manner similar to the preparation of chokecherries and dried.

The dried buffaloberries could be added to cornmeal porridge to produce *huunaaní'Is*. Gilmore collected a specimen of the berries and they are in the Smithsonian Institution collections.

According to Mrs. Redtail, "buffalo berries were also used as a mordant (a substance to help color stay in the material being dyed) for a native blue dye," but Gilmore could not determine which plant was used for this blue dye. Also, in the olden days, as John Box told Gilmore in 1924, "when the buffalo berries are ripe, they knew that the bison cows also were now fat."

In the semi-mythologized historical account of the Arikara heroine *PaaRIhná* Carries The Horn—also called *stIšaátu'* Ribs Woman and *staWIsaaNAhkatá* Yellow Cedar Woman—as narrated by both Lillian Brave (Parks 1991a:836–842) and Mary Gillette (Parks 1991a:1232–1236), the woman and her sister go across the river to pick *naáni'Is*. Carries The Horn has her sister hide under the bullboat for safety while she goes to pick the berries. While picking, she is attacked by Sioux (*sanánat*). In one account, she turns around and chases the Sioux that attacked her, managing to pull off his leggings in the process, which she displays as a trophy. In another account, she turns into a bear after the Sioux cut off her finger and she chases them away. In any case, as a story based in reality, this is another account showing the dangers of gathering wild plants away from the village (see also the description under *Amphicarpaea bracteata* above).

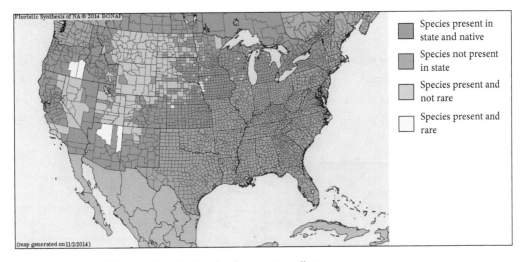

Figure 198. Map of U.S. counties with *Shepherdia argentea* collections.

Smilax herbacea L.

- **Carrion flower**
- *načiikaáhUx*, lit. "drinking wood"

Figure 199. The shiny seeds of carrion flower, *Smilax herbacea,* were used by putting them into rattles (typically made from gourds). Photograph by Michael Haddock. Used with permission.

The Arikara word form recorded by Gilmore tentatively appears to mean "drinking wood": *rak-* "wood" + *čiikaa* "drink" + *-hUx* "-ing". There is possibly a relationship with the word for "gourd", *načiikúxtš*. As Gilmore reports, the hard, shiny seeds of this plant were used by putting them into rattles (typically made from gourds). See also the name and entry for *Celastrus scandens* L.

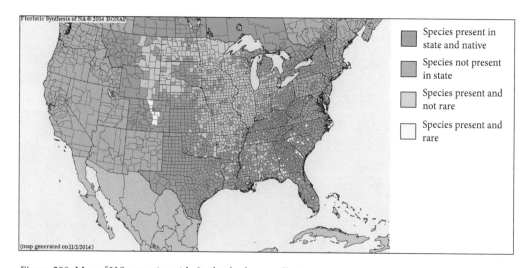

Figure 200. Map of U.S. counties with *Smilax herbacea* collections.

Spartina pectinata Bosc ex Link

- called *S. michauxiana* by Gilmore
- **Slough Grass** or **Prairie Cordgrass**
- *haaNUtčiWAhaánu'*, lit. "slough grass"
- *huhkáxIš*, lit. "hard grass"

Figure 201. The leaves and stems of cordgrass, *Spartina pectinata,* were also used for making mats, and this grass was also dried as horse feed. Photograph by Michael Haddock. Used with permission.

The first Arikara name is a compound of *haanuút-u'*, "Native dry grass" and *čiWAhaán-u'*, "slough, lake". This name relates to the grass normally being found in a slough, wet ravine, or lake edge. The second name is composed of *huún-u'* "grass" + *kaxiš* "hard", which may refer to the observation that the grass was hard to cut, according to Ella Waters (rec. 1976) (Parks 1970–1997).

The lower blades of this grass were used to make mats in a manner similar to the making of braided mats from **hiš** bulrush [see bulrush, *Schoenoplectus tabernaemontani*] .... The Arikara also cut this grass with their knives to make hay to feed their horses. It was bound in bundles to keep for winter (G).

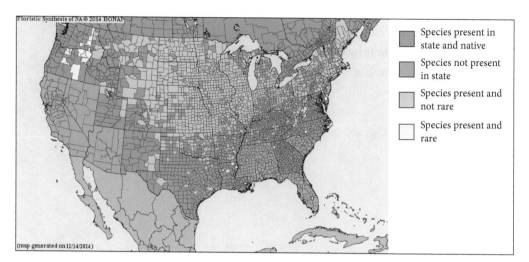

Figure 202. Map of U.S. counties with *Spartina pectinata* collections.

Sphaeralcea coccinea (Nutt.) Rydb.

- called *Malvastrum coccineum* by Gilmore
- **Scarlet globemallow** or **False red mallow**
- *paatAhuunuukaásu'*, in reference to the plant
- *paatAhuunuukaásu' sa'iítu'*, in reference to the flower

Figure 203. Scarlet globemallow (*Sphaeralcea coccinea*) is a very muscilagenous plant, used fresh and dried in a variety of medicines, including to stop the flow of blood. Photograph by Kelly Kindscher.

The Arikara name, *paatAhuunuukaásu'* means "cut vein": *paatAhuún-u'* "vein" + *ukaas* "cut". The name of the flower refers to an object on the end of a stalk or protrusion, but represents the only attested use of the word *sa'iít-u'* "on the end".

> The stems and leaves of this plant were dried, ground fine, and the resulting powder made into a paste in the mouth and applied as a plaster to a cut to stop bleeding.

In case of hemorrhage from a wound, a sufficient quantity of this paste was taken into the mouth and there with the saliva worked into a mucilaginous paste which was applied to stop the bleeding. The plant in all its parts was very mucilaginous (G).

This native Globemallow was also used as part of a postpartum hemorrhage treatment:

in case of postpartum hemorrhage the juice of the chokecherry is given to the patient to drink. Also in such cases the gum which exudes from the chokecherry tree (*Prunus virginiana*), *nakaaNUsčiísu'*, is triturated (finely ground) together with the root of scarlet globemallow and made into an infusion which is given as a drink. (Gilmore 1931a).

Ella Waters (rec. 1976, 1977) stated that

the root and flower of this plant were mixed with old Chokecherry resin (*nakaaNUsčiísu'*) and the mixture then used for treating diarrhea. It would also be mixed with bloodroot (*kAswáhAt*) to treat blood or nose hemorrhaging or diarrhea.

Also, "a small amount of powdered Globemallow would be stored in buckskin to maintain its potency" (Parks 1970–1997).

Figure 204. Map of U.S. counties with *Sphaeralcea coccinea* collections.

Symphoricarpos occidentalis Hook.

- **Western Snowberry** or **Buck brush, Wolfberry**
- *kaapiniwóx*, in reference to the plant
- *haakakoótu'*, lit. "sore mouth", in reference to the berry

Figure 205. The ripe, white fruits of the western snowberry, *Symphoricarpos occidentalis,* were used as a medicine to treat sores. Photograph by Craig Freeman. Used with permission.

"The name *kaapiniwóx* means 'broom'. It was so called because this brush was gathered into bundles to be used as brooms in sweeping the house floors and the ground about the doorways of the houses" (G). The "berries uses as medicine for sore mouth, or any sore" according to SteštAhkáta. This usage is the source of the name of the berry: *haaká-u'* "mouth" + *koot* "sore". Also this species, along with *čitapAtwáhAt* sandbar willow, *Salix interior*, were natural indicators of ground for growing corn, beans, and squash. And "when buck brush began to show new leaves in the spring, it was time to plant corn" (G).

In William Deane, Jr.'s story of Coyote and the Jerusalem artichokes (Parks 1991a:1259)—and see the entry for *Helianthus tuberosus, tšuúxIt,* above—Coyote tries grabbing hold of a *kaapiniwóx* buckbrush to keep from flying off the ground because of the flatulence caused by the *tšuúxIt.* The buckbrush is unable to withstand the force of the fart, however, and Coyote pulls it out of the ground when he flies up, hurting himself when he lands again.

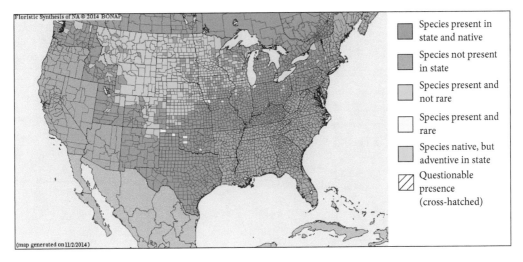

Figure 206. Map of U.S. counties with *Symphoricarpos occidentalis* collections.

Thalictrum sp.

- **Meadow rue**
- *škanítš*, lit. "little many hands"

Figure 207. Meadown rue, *Thalictrum dasycarpon*, was a perfume, applied by men to their clothing, which was supposed to be a love charm that would attract women. Photograph by Michael Haddock. Used with permission.

The Arikara name of the Meadow rue means "little many hands": *íš-u'* "hand" + *-kani* "many" + *-tš* "diminutive suffix". The name probably refers to the small, hand-shaped leaves. See also the description of the name for *Actaea rubra* above.

"The seeds of *Thalictrum* were used for perfume by men, being chewed and put on most of the clothing. It was also supposed to be a love charm which would attract women" (G).

According to Ella Waters (rec. 1976, ca. 1979), "the top part and seeds of Meadow rue *škanítš* were mixed with Sweetgrass *haaNUtwaraakAhá'*, which were boiled together into a 'tea' that was used to wash one's hair. When so washed, one maintained black hair, it was believed. The solution also gave a pleasant fragrance to the hair" (Parks 1970–1997).

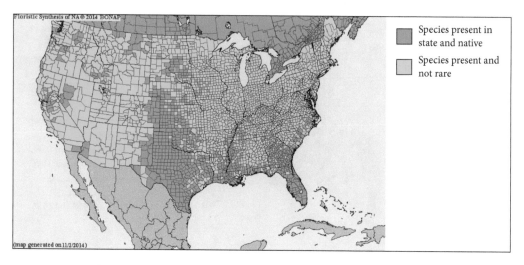

Figure 208. Map of U.S. counties with *Thalictrum species* collections.

Typha latifolia L.

- **Cat-tail** or **Broadleaf cattail**
- *čiriNAsiínu'*, in reference to the plant or the fruit
- *hIštaátu'*, *hIškatóx*, in reference to the stalk itself
- *hItkaataátš*, in reference to the rootstalks

Figure 209. The cat-tail, *Typha latifolia*, had many uses—from its roots being eaten as a rich food, to its fluffy heads being used as adsorbent material instead of baby diapers. Photograph by Michael Haddock. Used with permission.

Gilmore states that "[t]he name, *čiriNAsiínu'*, means 'eye-inflammation,' from the effect on a person's eyes when the light, downy seeds of the plant are blown into one's eyes by the wind" (G). The reference to eyes is transparent (*čiriík-u'* "eye" + *ran-* "plural"), but the part that would mean "inflammation" has not been found elsewhere (unless it derives from *siin* "work"). The related Pawnee name for the plant is *kiriktacarus* "itchy eyes". "They call the rootstock of the cat-tail *hItkaataáts*, 'tallow', because it tastes like tallow. The Arikara people, especially the boys, dug the rootstocks to use as food because of their rich, agreeable taste" (G). The term for the stalk itself, *hIštaátu'*, simply means "reed stalk", while *hIškatóx* means "flat reed".

> When the cat-tail heads were just ripe they were gathered to use in finishing the dressing of the tanned deerskins. The fine, granular, chaffy seeds were plucked from the cat-tails and spread upon a tanned deerskin pegged down upon the ground. When a thick layer of cat-tail seeds had been thus deposited another deerskin was spread over the first, having at each end a stick attached horizontally for a handle. Then some cobblestones were laid upon the upper deerskin to hold it down. The process was operated by two women sitting upon the ground facing each other with the deerskins between them. They each grasped with both hands one of the sticks fastened at either end of the upper deerskin, and each alternately drew the upper deerskin towards herself; thus it was drawn forth and back, with the stones holding it down and furnishing friction for the buffing of the two skins by the fine downy cat-tail seeds between them, ultimately giving to both skins a very fine surface finish. Obviously this work must be done inside the house, or if outside, only at such times as the weather was perfectly calm, for the slightest breeze would blow away the cat-tail down (G).

Gilmore wrote a paper called "The Cattail Game of Arikara Children" (1928). Much of the information for this children's game was from interviews of an elder, Albert Simpson, whom Gilmore interviewed in August 1926 and he stated that:

> Children used cat-tail in an active game. Three long leaves of cat-tail were plaited together in such fashion as to form a cross. To form the cross one leaf was laid down and then another leaf was attached at right angles by bending one end squarely about the middle of the first leaf. The third leaf was attached in like manner, but extending at right angles on the opposite side of the first leaf from the second. This game might be played by girls alone or by boys and girls together. Four children would step up to the cross old leaf blades and join hands diagonally over it. Thus holding hands they must dance rapidly about the cross, being careful to step over and not upon the crossed leaves. If one should

misstep and stumble upon one of the leaves all would immediately loose hands, the one who made the misstep would run away, and the other three would give chase, each armed with a cat-tail stalk. With these they struck the fleeing one if able to overtake him. When the fugitive was struck the cat-tail clubs shed their downy seeds and the air was full of flying down. The children had a merry time.

Another use of cat-tail was for the care of young infants. When a new little member of the family was expected all the female relatives of the mother busied themselves to help in gathering a supply of cat-tail down to provide for the expected need. No White mother takes greater care in the preparation of the layette [a collection of clothing for a new born] for the advent of her darling than did the Indian mother and her relatives. Cat-tail down was used to pad the cushioned lining of the cradle to be a soft nest for the little one. The Indian mother in old times had no cotton diapers to provide for her infant as the White mother has, but in place of these she provided a sufficient supply of cat-tail down to be used as an absorbent pad within the soft-tanned deerskin swaddling, a supply sufficient for renewing at every need of change. The deerskin swaddling was not wrapped diaper-fashion as White people do, but was wrapped cylindrically, band-like about the hips and thighs of the infant, with a soft pad of cat-tail down laid under the hips and between the thighs.

Cattail rootstalks were considered a good rich food as "the Arikara people, especially the boys, dug the rootstocks to use as food because of their rich agreeable taste." The elder, John Box, told that the cattail was also a phenological indicator, and "when at home, they used the cattails ripening to know that the buffalo bulls are now fat; and when the buffalo berries are ripe, they knew that the cows also were now fat."

Figure 210. Map of U.S. counties with *Typha latifolia* collections.

Ulmus spp. (probably *Ulmus rubra* or *U. americana*)

- **Elm, Slippery elm** or **American elm**
- *nakás*, lit. "gray wood"
- *sataáku'*, lit. "basket tree"

Figure 211. The inner bark of elm, (*Ulmus americana,* in the picture) was used in strips to tie bundles. Photograph by Craig Freeman. Used with permission.

There are two Arikara terms for Elm trees, which appear to represent two different species. The more common word, *nakás*, denotes the American Elm (*Ulmus Americana*) and is composed of *rak-* ~ *haak-* "wood" + *kaas* "gray". The word *sataáku'* means "basket wood/tree", a compound of *saát-u'* "basket" + *rak-* ~ *haak-* "wood/tree", in reference to the use described below. This may refer to the Slippery Elm (*Ulmus rubra*).

Ella Waters (rec. 1973, 1976) said of *sataáku'* that "the bark was used for working baskets and tying bundles" (Parks 1970–1997). The elm bark used was likely of young limbs, which can easily be slipped off the wood, not the older bark, which is far more corky.

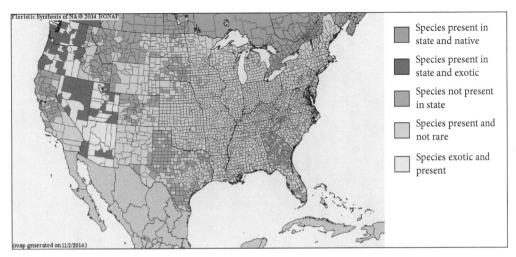

Figure 212. Map of U.S. counties with *Ulmus* species collections.

Viburnum lentago L.

- **Black haw, Nanny berry**
- *ištAhnaanákUx*, in generic reference or to refer to the fruits
- *ištAhnaanákUx iinatawaáWI*, in reference to the tree, lit. "where the black haws grow on it"

Figure 213. The fruit of the black haw, *Viburnum lentago,* was boiled and dried for later food use. Photograph by D. Herman. Used with permission.

There is no transparent etymology for the long name of the Black haw fruit. The name for the tree includes a participle *iinatawaáWI* meaning "there where they grow": *ii-* "there" + *na...wi* "locative participle" + *-waa* "grow (plural)".

Ella Waters (rec. ca. 1979) describes that "the black haw fruit was dried and stored. Later it was boiled. The seed of the black haw was put on one's face to give the appearance of having a mole. Girls did this for cosmetic purposes" (Parks 1970–1997).

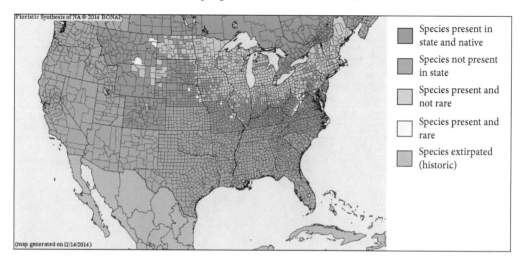

Species present in state and native

Species not present in state

Species present and not rare

Species present and rare

Species extirpated (historic)

Figure 214. Map of U.S. counties with *Viburnum lentago* collections.

Vitis riparia Michx.

- **Wild grape** or **Riverbank grape**
- *tšús*, in generic reference to the plant or to the fruit
- *tšUstaátu'*, referring to the grapevine

Figure 215. The fruits of the wild grape, *Vitis riparia,* which follow the flowers pictured here, were enjoyed fresh or dried. Photograph by Craig Freeman. Used with permission.

It is noted that Gilmore also lists a word *sčeekaraáku'* for the leaf for this entry. However, this is the generic term for "leaf" and there is no other evidence that it has any particularly unique association with the Wild Grape leaf.

> The fruit of the wild grapes were eaten raw, cooked into a sauce, or the fruit was dried to store for future use. The leaves of the wild grape were used for playful divination by girls and young women. For this purpose a young woman, being in the woods where grapes abounded, would pick a grape leaf at random while thinking of her sweetheart. If she finds the mid-rib of the leaf branched in four veins she may trustfully accept him, but if only two veins are found in the leaf she must not marry him or they will have bad luck (G).

In the story of Coyote and the Artichokes, as told by Lillian Brave (Parks 1991a:854–855), as Coyote is beset by explosive flatulence, after eating *tšuúxIt* artichokes, and keeps being launched into the air, a *tšús* takes pity on him. Coyote takes hold of the grapevine and it successfully anchors him to the ground so he doesn't hurt himself.

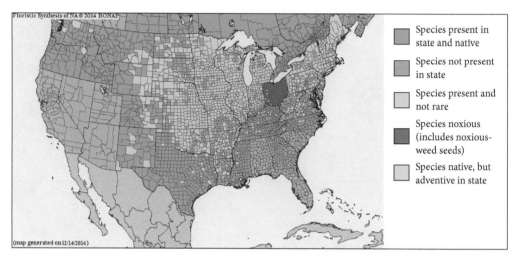

Floristic Synthesis of NA © 2014 BONAP

(map generated on 12/14/2014)

Species present in state and native

Species not present in state

Species present and not rare

Species noxious (includes noxious-weed seeds)

Species native, but adventive in state

Figure 216. Map of U.S. counties with *Vitis riparia* collections.

Xanthium strumarium L.

- **Cocklebur**
- *piira'aátUx, piira'aátu'*

Figure 217. The large spiny burs of cocklebur, *Xanthium strumarium*, were used as part of a medicine. Photograph by Kelly Kindscher.

According to Ella Waters (rec. ca. 1979), this refers to

the large bur which grows in the woods [*Xanthium*], not the small bur growing on the prairie [*Cenchus*], and is used in medicine. When dry, it was used to puncture the jaw of a person who had a crooked mouth, or more accurately, a crooked jaw. Medicine—a powder of unspecified roots—was then applied to the pricked area (Parks 1970–1997).

See the previous entry on *Glycyrrhiza* for comments on the etymology of the Arikara name. The two variant pronunciations do not reflect significantly different meanings.

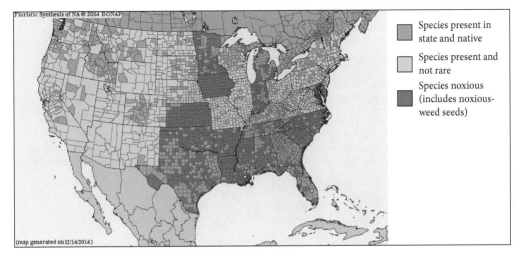

Figure 218. Map of U.S. counties with *Xanthium strumarium* collections.

Yucca glauca Nutt.

- **Yucca, Spanish bayonet,** or **Soapweed yucca**
- *sačíínatA*

Figure 219. The root of yucca, *Yucca glauca,* was used for medicine, tanning hides, and for soap. Photograph by Kelly Kindscher.

"The root was used for medicine, tanning hides, and for soap" (G). Also, yucca smoke (likely from a burned root) was used to treat earache (Melvin R. Gilmore Papers, Box 3, Field Notebooks).

Angela Plante (rec. 1987, 1996) and Lillian Brave (rec. 1987) presented a description of an otherwise unidentified root which they attributed to the Arikara name *sačiínatA*, but better fits the profile of *Cucurbita foetidissima* (see entry above). William Deane, Jr. (rec. ca. 1979) states that *sačiínatA*, again unidentified but for its Arikara name, "grows in Montana." (Parks 1970–1997). The *sačiínatA* was thus apparently rare enough to Arikaras by the mid-to-late twentieth century that only cursory details of it could be identified and its English name equivalent remained elusive. Ella Waters (rec. 1976) even hypothesized that it could refer to Wild Hops (*Humulus lupulus*), although she later (rec. 1977, ca. 1979) seems to have been uncertain (Parks 1970–1997).

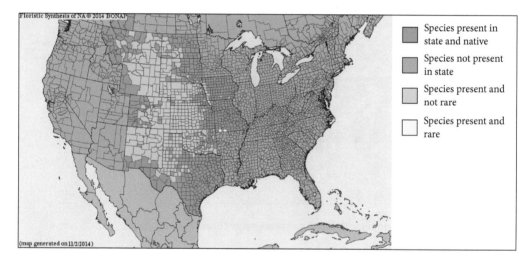

Figure 220. Map of U.S. counties with *Yucca glauca* collections.

Lichen

Letharia vulpina (L.) Wainio
- **Wolf lichen**

This lichen was "used by Crows and other tribes within its range and imported by other tribes outside. Specimen and information from Mrs. Butcher, an Arikara woman living at Armstrong, Fort Berthold Reservation, North Dakota." It was used "for a yellow dye, made by steeping in water with the quills or other material to be dyed." Gilmore collected this lichen and it is part of the Smithsonian Institution collections, NMAI #122979.

Mushrooms

Calvatia sp.
- **Puffball**
- *kaáhA*

The Arikara name for the Puffball may also be used as a generic term for any mushrooms.

> When firm and white, the puffball was boiled for food. And when ripe, the spores were used like talcum powder on infants, under the armpit, between thighs, and behind the ears. Also used as a styptic (to stop bleeding), especially on the umbilicus of a new born (G).

Also immediately after the birth of a child, the Arikara midwife would

> cut off the umbilical cord at a length reaching to the child's knees... Then she twists up the cord and coils it spirally about the navel and leaves the end turned upward. A ripe puffball is clamped on and bound with a bandage of soft tanned buffalo hide. After three or four days the cord will be dried up and drop off (Gilmore 1931a).

Also, "in case of inflammation of the breasts, some root of *škanikaatít* red baneberry, *Actaea rubra*, is pulverized and mixed with the powdery mass of spores of a ripe puffball to make a poultice to apply. It is said this quickly relieves the pain and swelling" (G).

Ustilago maydis
- **Corn smut**
- *katawárus*

The Sahnish name means "bump on the side": *kata-* "against a vertical surface" + *-waruus* "bump".

Corn smut was a food for the Arikara and although it comes from corn ears being infected, it

> did no damage, for if it destroyed a small percentage of the corn it in itself substituted another desirable article of food. When firm and white, before the maturing of the spores, it was cooked with squash both fresh and dried and put away for winter, when it was cooked with dried squash (G).

A Mushroom (unidentified)

- *nakAsItkaataáts̆*, lit. "wood root tallow"
- *áxkAs*

The first Arikara name means "wood root tallow" (or perhaps "Elm tallow": *rak- ~ haak-* "wood, tree" + *kás-u'* "herb, root" + *hItkaataá-ts̆* "tallow, suet", but cf. *nakás* "Elm" (*Ulmus spp.*). The second name, *áxkAs*, is homophonous with the word for "sinew". It is unclear whether or not these names referred to the same species of fungus.

Albert Simpson reported in 1926 that this was "a large bracket fungus, found on old downed logs. The tender young part was boiled with meat, corn, beans, squash, etc. for a stew. [It was] said to be like suet." This may be the edible mushroom oyster mushroom, *Pleurotus ostreatus*, known from North Dakota. It also grows on dead Elm trees.

Angela Plante (rec. 1996) reported of *áxkAs* that "these mushrooms were cut up and cooked (for food)" (Parks 1970–1997).

Large, thick white mushroom that grows on trees

- *áxkAs*
- Same pronunciation as "sinew", but different meaning.

Angela Plante, an Arikara native speaker reported in 1996 that "these mushrooms were cut up and cooked" (for food).

Note both of these may have been the same mushroom, or they might be something different.

Section 3.

1. Wild Plants with Ethnographic Notes

Dry grass, Hay
- *haanuútu'*

Originally, this Arikara word referred to the dry grass on the Plains that was eaten by buffalo. It has been extended to also refer to hay (Parks 1970–1997).

Little bluestem, Prairie Beardgrass
- *Schizachyrium scoparium* (Michx.) Nash
- *huhwáhat, huhpáhAt, haaNUtwáhAt*, lit. "red grass"

The Arikara names are the same as big bluestem, *Andopogon gerardii* (see above) and according to Ella Waters (rec. ca. 1979), it was considered a "hard grass," and not eaten by horses or cattle (Parks 1970–1997).

Plant that hides when the ground vibrates (*unidentified*)
- *hunahkanií'u'*, lit. "earth penis"

The Arikara name is comprised of *hunaán-u'* "earth" + *kanií-u'* "penis" + *-u'*. This name possibly derives from the way that "this plant leaves a wet spot where the plant 'urinates,'" according to Lillian Brave and Angela Plante (rec. 1987). This plant was used for medicine. The name might also refer to the upright, phallic-shaped mounds in the Badlands where it was found (Parks 1970–1997).

Root species (*unidentified*)
- *kAsteešaánu'*, lit. "chief herb/root"

The Arikara name is derived from *kás-u'* "root, herb" + *neešaán-u'* "chief".

William Deane, Jr. (rec. 1975) describes this unidentified plant as growing "around Red Lake, MN." Ella Waters (rec. 1976) reported that "it was one of the primary medicines, mixed with nearly all other medicines" (Parks 1970–1997). It may refer to one of the plants described in the above manuscript, but it is ambiguous as to which one.

Stinging nettle
- *Urtica dioica* L.
- *kootIhkatáWA, kotkatáWA*, lit. "sore going against"

The Arikara name appears to derive from *koot* "rot, die, sore" + *kata-* "against" + *wan* "go", probably derived from the irritation it causes.

Ella Waters (rec. 1981) describes the plant of this Arikara name as "a tall spindly weed which produces itchy rash, like poison ivy" (Parks 1970–1997). This description fits *Urtica dioica*, but the reference remains uncertain.

Plant species *(unidentified)*

- *nakaraakAxaačipiriínu'*, lit. "young dog (or horse) leaf"

The Arikara name ambiguously means "young dog leaf" or "young horse leaf": *nakaraák-u'* "tea leaf" + *axaa-* "dog, horse" + *čipiriin* "new, young". The former name may be the more likely, if it is in reference to *xaačipiriínu'*, the Young Dog Society.

Ella Waters (rec. ca. 1979) describes this plant as having "a long, flat leaf, about 1.5 inches long, which grows flat on dry ground in a slough. It is green and turns red in the fall. It was dried and used for tea, but not used medicinally" (Parks 1970–1997). This description is not sufficient for certain identification of the plant, however.

Hop vine (*Humulus lupulus*)

- *teenít*, lit. "twiner"

The Arikara name appears to be based on the verb *ut...teeniik* "be wrapped or wound around". Gilmore explicitly reports that this vine has "no known use" (G).

2. Botanical Terms and Species with No Ethnobotanical Information

Tree mushroom

- *ahkAsáro'*

The Arikara name appears to translate literally to "tooth pick".

Tobacco

- *hahnaaWIškaánu', naaWIškaánu'*, lit. "smoking (wood)"

The Arikara name is a compound that refers to smoking: (*haak-* "wood" +) *naawíš-u'* "smoke" + *kan* "consume". It refers to any type of tobacco, although there is a special term, *saakawíʔu'* for "Indian" tobacco that the Arikara raised and traded for. See *Nicotiana quadrivalvis* Pursh. above.

Dead grass

- *haaNUtkoótu'*, lit. "dead grass"

The Arikara name is comprised of *haanuút-u'* "grass" + *koot* "dead, die". This term just refers to any dead grass.

Vine, Climbing plant

- *haxtAsawanúx*, lit. "climbing around string"

The name is a verbal compound: *háx-tš* "string" + *ran-* "plural" + *tawanuu* "climb around" + *-hux* "-ing". This is a generic term that applies to any climbing plant.

Reed species (*unidentified*)

- *hiškatóx*, lit. "flat reed/rush" (*híš* "bulrush, reed" + *katoox* "flat")

Chairmaker's rush, Three-cornered rush

- *Schoenoplectus americanus* (Pers.)Volkart ex Schinz & R. Keller. (Perhaps also a sedge, *Carex* sp.)
- *hIšwaahawá*, lit. "cornered reed"

The Arikara name refers to its three-cornered form: *híš* "reed, bulrush" + *waahawaar* "cornered". Exact traditional usage is unknown.

Algae, Moss (on stagnant water)

- *hoowiranaanuúxu'*, lit. "fuzz on the water" (*hoowi-* "(appears) in/on water" + *ran-* "plural" + *raanux* "hairy")

Water plant, Plant that grows underwater
- *hoowíʼu'*, lit. "(appears) in/on the water" (*huu-* "in/on water" + *awí-u'* "image")

Pasque flower, Cutleaf Anemone, Crocus
- *Pulsatilla patens* (L.) Mill.
- *huNAhpaáku'*

Grass (generic), Hay, Weeds
- *huúnu'*

Poison ivy
- *Toxicodendron radicans* (L.) Kuntze
- *kaanánax*

Buffalo sod
- *kAstAhahkatít*, lit. "black sod" (*kAstAhaán-u'* "sod" + *katiit* "black")
- This term refers to the large chunks of sod that buffalo would kick up.

Sweet cicely
- *Osmorhiza claytonii* (Michx.) C.B. Clarke
- *kAstanáha'*, lit. "buffalo root" (*kás-u'* "root, herb" + *tanáha'* "buffalo")

Green grass
- *kataánu'*

Vine
- *naakAxiitaátu'*, lit. "wood bag plant" (*rak-* "wood" + *kAxií-u'* "bag" + *taát-u'* "stem, plant")
- *natareepiíNU*, lit. "the tied one" (*na-…-u* "participle" + *-tareepiin* "tied")

"Real tree" (*unidentified*)
- *NAhnaaNIšíšu'*, lit. "real tree" (*rak-* "wood" + *naaNIšíš-u'* "real, prototypical, genuine"
It is not certain what type of tree this referred to. It would have been a prominent and fairly common type of (deciduous) tree, serving as the prototypical species of tree.

Squirreltail
- *Elymus elymoides* (Raf.) Swezey
- *piišiʼát*

Oak tree, Bur Oak

- *Quercus macrocarpa* Michx.
- *skaáNUx*

The Arikara name *skaáNUx* also refers to the walnut and, by extension, nuts in general.

Black walnut

- *skaaNUxkaátit*, lit. "dark walnut" (*skaáNUx* "walnut" + *kaatiit* "dark")

Scum

- *suusá'u'*

Prairie mushroom, Toadstool

- *škaawanúx*, lit. "hand going around inside" (*íš-u'* "hand" + *kaa-* "inside" + *wanuu* "go around" + *-x* "-ing")

This mushroom is described by Ella Waters (rec. 1976) as growing in manure (Parks 1970–1997). The Arikara term also refers to a clown or a nosy, inquisitive person who pries into things.

Mold, Mildew

- *uxkoótu'*, lit. "rotten hair" (*uúx-u'* "hair" + *koot* "rot, die")

Young cottonwood

- *WAxačipiriínu'*, lit. "new/young cottonwood" (*WAxaák-u'* "cottonwood" + *-čipiriin* "new")

Quaking aspen, White poplar

- *Populus tremuloides* Michx.
- *WAxAhtaaká*, lit. "white cottonwood" (*WAxaák-u'* "cottonwood" + *taakaan* "white")

3. Names for Parts of Plants

Xylem — *Asškaáwi'u'* – It was bored out of a branch for making a pipe stem.

Root — *AxkAsaáwi'u'*

Root, Sprout — *Axkásu'*

Branch, Limb — *haačitawí'u'*

Tree sap — *hahnačiisu'*

Trunk — *hahtatwaruú'u'*

Tree stump — *hahtarikuúsu'*

Small branch — *haakAxIsapaáku'*

Tree branch — *haakáxu', haakAxká'u'*

Twig, Branch from which fruit hangs — *haakIsapaáxu'*

Tree bark — *haakIskuúxu'* – Includes cottonwood bark, which was used in winter to feed
     horses. They were kept in the earth lodge at night, in a corral on the left side by
     the door. They were put outside during the day.

Chaff, Wheat kernel shells — *haričiitIskuúxu'*

Bud — *kanipiíku'*

Root (in the ground) — *kAsukaawí'u'*

Straw — *ka'ístš* – also used for a tray woven of reeds or for a small, flat basket

Corn tassel — *naaNAhíšu'* – It was made into a tea and used for medicine. It was mixed with
     other roots and administered for hemorrhaging.

Sprout of root or vegetable — *naáxu'* – used particularly for corn and squash sprouts

Tree wart — *načiRIhtá'u'*

Seed, Planting seed — *načiriíku'*

Pine cone — *načíšu' kaanipiíku'*

Flower — *NAhkaaxíšu'*

Tea, tea leaves — *nakaraáku'*

Root of a tree or woody bush — *nakAsukaawí'u'*

Rotten log — *nakoótu'*

Tree top, Top of a bush — *naparaanuúxu'*

Wood, stick, pole — *nátš*

Leaf — *sčeekaraáku'*

Big walnut — *skaaNUxkúsu'*

Fruit — *nohtAhaniwaará'u'*

Inner bark of tree, especially cottonwood tree – *skataátu'* – Used for horse feed, and for tying
     bundles or baskets

Rind, Peel, Integument — *skuúxu'* – refers to skin or outer layer of any kind

Stalk, Stem, Plant (generic) — *taátu'*

Woods, Forest — *waraá'u'* – used especially in the forms *waraákAt* "in the woods" and
     waraačeékAt "in the thick woods"

4. Pronunciation Guide

Arikara language examples in this paper are presented in the relatively standardized orthography developed in the 1970s by linguist Douglas Parks and members of the Arikara community. The system uses fairly standard Americanist transcription conventions—differing from the International Phonetic Alphabet (IPA) in only two characters—with some simple amendments for practical purposes. Once the conventions are known, pronunciation of written Arikara words is almost wholly interpretable.

The following table presents the consonants of Arikara. From left to right, the table shows the letter used in the Arikara writing system, its IPA value, an English example illustrating an approximation of the Arikara sound, an example Arikara word containing the sound, along with the meaning of that word.

Arikara Letter	IPA value	English example	Arikara example	
p	[p]	s<u>p</u>ot (between <u>p</u>ot and <u>b</u>ot)	p̣iíra'u'	baby
t	[t]	s<u>t</u>op (between <u>t</u>op and <u>d</u>ot)	ṭaapáhA<u>t</u>	red-tail deer
k	[k]	s<u>c</u>oop (between <u>c</u>oop and <u>g</u>oop)	ḳaáḳa'	crow, raven
č	[tʃ]	between <u>ch</u>op and <u>j</u>ot	čituú'u'	all, every
s	[s]	<u>s</u>oup	ṣápat	woman
š	[ʃ]	<u>sh</u>ip	šakuúnu'	sun, day
x	[x]	Not in English, a scratchy "k" sound, like Spanish <u>j</u>ota or German Ba<u>ch</u>	x̣aátš	dog
h	[h]	<u>h</u>ot	ḥatuúnu'	road, path
n	[n]	<u>n</u>oo<u>n</u>	ṇú'	turkey
r	[ɾ]	la<u>dd</u>er, or like Spanish pe<u>r</u>o	taṛá	twins
w	[w]	<u>w</u>in	ẉiísu'	heart
'	[ʔ]	Catch in the throat in the middle of "uh‿oh"	ookaa'aasí'u'	shade

Arikara vowels are pronounced consistently, unlike in English writing. Vowels may be short, written with one vowel letter, or long, written with a doubled vowel letter. A long vowel is pronounced about the same as its short counterpart, but is held for approximately twice as long.

Arikara Letter	IPA value	English example	Arikara example	
i	[i ~ ɪ]	between b<u>ea</u>t and b<u>i</u>t	p<u>i</u>táru'	ant
ii	[iː]	b<u>ea</u>d	w<u>ii</u>tA	man
e	[e]	between b<u>ai</u>t and b<u>e</u>t	<u>e</u>tčiísu'	milk
ee	[eː]	between p<u>ai</u>d and b<u>e</u>d	n<u>ee</u>kawí'u'	door
a	[a ~ ɐ]	between t<u>o</u>p and b<u>u</u>t	<u>a</u>tⁱn<u>á</u>'	mother
aa	[aː]	r<u>o</u>d	ak<u>aá</u>nu'	lodge, house
o	[o]	r<u>o</u>pe	n<u>o</u>htsAhaniwaáRA	soda
oo	[oː]	r<u>o</u>be	n<u>oo</u>xíni'	ten
u	[u ~ ʊ]	between b<u>oo</u>t and p<u>u</u>t	n<u>ú</u>t	snake
uu	[uː]	b<u>oo</u>ed	n<u>uu</u>tawáčeš	alligator

Long vowels are written, and pronounced, as short vowels at the end of a word or in a closed syllable (when a consonant comes at the end of the syllable). An accent mark over a vowel indicates that that vowel is stressed: the emphasis of the word goes on that vowel. The accent is written over the second vowel letter in a long vowel.

Arikara short vowels [*i, a, u*] get devoiced, or "whispered," when they <u>don't</u> have an accent and occur in predictable positions: 1) at the end of an utterance; 2) before any <u>coda</u> consonant except ' [a consonant at the end of a syllable, limited to *t, s, š, x, h* in Arikara]; and, 3) before a (fricative) consonant: *s, š, x, h*. Long vowels never get whispered, even when they get shortened as described above. The vowels *e* and *o* in Arikara always behave like long vowel, and never get whispered. A whispered vowel is written with a capital letter. If the (sonorant) consonants *n, r,* or *w* come before a whispered vowel, they also get whispered, and written with a capital letter. There is no English equivalent, except when one actually whispers.

Arikara Letter	IPA value	Arikara example	
I	i̥	h<u>I</u>štaahíšu'	breath
A	ḁ	ásk<u>A</u>t	above
U	u̥	čirík<u>U</u>	Oh my!
N	n̥	siiná<u>NI</u>	friend
R	ɾ̥	čí<u>RU</u>t	lizard
W	w̥	síš<u>WA</u>	Let's go (you and I)!

Because of this significant use of capitalization to mark pronunciation, we avoid writing capital letters on Arikara words at the beginning of sentences, so as not to cause confusion.

For accurate pronunciation, readers should also be aware of combinations of sounds:

- The common noun ending -*tš* is a shortened form of -*čIš* and is pronounced exactly like English "ch" in <u>ch</u>ur<u>ch</u> (IPA [tʃʰ]).
- When a short *i* or *u* vowel comes between *t* and *n*, and is not accented, the vowel often gets "swallowed," which is written with a superscript letter: *tⁱn, tᵘn*. At the beginning of an utterance, the *tⁱ* or *tᵘ* are completely silent: *tⁱnaáku'* "gun" is pronounced [*naáku'*]. If a vowel comes before the *t*, though, the *tⁱn* and *tᵘn* will sound like the "ton" in American English bu<u>tton</u>. Arikara *atⁱná'* "mother" thus sounds like "<u>button</u> <u>knot</u>," without the "b" or ending "t" (IPA [ɐtʔn̩ná?]).
- When a whispered vowel is followed by a fricative consonant [s, š, x, h], the vowel will be subtle and may just sound like a long version of that consonant: *AsIšUhúhnini'* "on one's mind" often sounds like [<u>ssšš</u>*húhnini'*]. If the consonant after the whispered vowel is *h*, the combination will sound like an aspirated (breathy) version of the consonant that comes before the vowel: *tAhuúnu'* "flint" sounds like English "toon newt," with the English breathy "t" (IPA [tʰú:nu?]).

Related to the previous point, if the whispered vowel is *I* or *U* and the consonant that follows is *h* or *x*, then the combination will have a "y"-like sound with *I* or a "w"-like sound with *U*. The beginning of the word *tIhútA* "It is windy" sounds like a breathy "ty," something like "<u>ty</u>oot" (with a whispered *A* at the end), or IPA [tʰʸútạ]. The beginning of *kUxaánu'* "bed" sounds like a scratchy breathy "kw" or "qu", something like "quah-newt," or IPA [kxʷá:nu?].

Appendix 1: Arikara Ethnobotany Plant Species List

Species Names	Common Name	Type of Use	Uses
Acer negundo L.	boxelder	Manufacture	handles for hoes
Achillea millefolium L.	common yarrow	Medicine	used together with red baneberry for sore eyes
Acorus americanus (Raf.) Raf.	calamus	Medicine	rhizomes for toothache, protection from danger and rattle snakes
Actaea rubra (Aiton) Willd.	red baneberry	Medicine	childbirth, postpartum, and newborn medical care; root infusion for headache or cold
Agastache foeniculum (Pursh) Kuntze	wild anise	Food, Perfume, Medicine	perfuming clothing, blankets, eagle wing fans; cooling tea drink; remedy for fever
Allium spp.	onion	Food	cooked by boiling in water then consumed in soup
Amaranthus spp.	amaranth	Hunting	seeds used as lure for birds
Amelanchier alnifolia (Nutt.) Nutt. ex M. Roem.	juneberry	Food, Dye	mordant
Amorpha fruticosa L.	false indigo bush	Manufacture, Incense	arrow shafts
Amorpha nana Nutt.	dwarf false indigo	Medicine, Craft	styptic; embroidery design
Amphicarpaea bracteata (L.) Fernald	ground bean	Food	a food, collected from the cache of mice
Andropogon gerardii Vitman	big bluestem	Manufacture	roof thatch, lining storage pits, rope fibers, seedling starter, children's arrow shafts
Anemone cylindrica A. Gray	cylindric anemone	Manufacture	down used for sanitary care absorbent padding for infants
Anemone virginiana L.	anemone	Manufacture	down used for sanitary care absorbent padding for infants
Apocynum cannabinum L.	dogbane	Medicine, Manufacture	ingredient in medicine for rousing a patient in a stupor; cordage
Arctostaphylos uva-ursi (L.) Spreng.	kinnikinnick	Smoking	dried leaves incorporated into smoking mix with tobacco
Artemisia dracunculus L.	tarragon	Medicine	Mixed with other medicines and used to wash sores
Artemisia frigida Willd.	prairie sagewort	Medicine	vapor bath
Artemisia longifolia Nutt.	long-leafed wormwood	Medicine, Manufacture	bedding, mats
Artemisia ludoviciana Nutt.	white sagebrush	Medicine, Hunting	vapor bath; mask human scent when trapping an eagle

Species Names	Common Name	Type of Use	Uses
Artemisia tridentata Nutt.	big sagebrush	Medicine, Manufacture	pipe-cleaners and stems, basketry, earrings, horse equipment
Asclepias syriaca L.	common milkweed	Food, Medicine	cooked young leaves, bud clusters, young seed pods; remedy for insufficient lactation
Astragalus crassicarpus Nutt.	ground plum milkvetch	Craft	used by children when dried as beads, strung for necklaces
Atriplex argentea Nutt.	silverscale saltbush	Food, Medicine	stems and leaves cooked with other foods for seasoning
Calamagrostis canadensis (Michx.) P. Beauv.	bluejoint	Medicine	blades of grass used to treat trachoma and cataracts, sharpness also used for cutting
Calamovilfa longifolia (Hook.) Scribn.	prairie sandreed	Manufacture	pipe-cleaner; stalks worn as honor badge
Celastrus scandens L.	American bittersweet	Manufacture	rattle making
Chenopodium album L.	lamb's-quarter	Food	cooked as greens
Cirsium undulatum (Nutt.) Spreng.	wavyleaf thistle	Craft	down was dyed and twisted into a fine yarn to use in embroidery
Clematis ligusticifolia Nutt.	virgin's bower	Games	children used to make play wigs and regalia
Cornus amomum Mill.	silky dogwood	Smoking	inner bark used for smoking
Cornus sericea L.	red osier dogwood	Medicine, Smoking	inner bark used for smoking; berries eaten as remedy for huskiness of the voice
Crataegus spp.	hawthorn	Craft	thorns were used as awls
Cucurbita foetidissima Kunth	Missouri gourd	Medicine	dried root pulverized, remedy for dropsy, ulcers, sores, swelling and other ills
Cyclachaena xanthiifolia (Nutt.) Fresen.	marsh elder	Food	young tender leaves and stems cooked for greens, tasted somewhat like string beans
Dalea sp.	white prairie clover	Food	sweet root eaten by children
Echinacea angustifolia DC.	echinacea	Game, Medicine	game of skill played by children twirling the stalks
Elaeagnus commutata Bernh. ex Rydb.	silverberry	Drink	tea, comforting table beverage
Equisetum sp.	horsetail	Manufacture, horse food	horse food; finely abrasive material for polishing objects
Ericameria nauseosa (Pall. ex Pursh) G.L. Nesom & Baird	rubber rabbitbrush	Medicine	wash made from tops for saddle-sores, also a cleaning brush for washing horses after running

Species Names	Common Name	Type of Use	Uses
Erysimum asperum (Nutt.) DC.	western wallflower	Medicine	used for all wounds (gunshot, arrow, cuts, etc.)
Fraxinus pennsylvanica Marshall	green ash	Hunting, Manufacture	used to make a deer decoy
Galium triflorum Michx.	fragrant bedstraw	Perfume	made from whole plant
Glycyrrhiza lepidota Pursh	American licorice	Medicine	burrs used to clean sores or skin by abrasion; root for headache, diarrhea, hoarseness
Grindelia squarrosa (Pursh) Dunal	curlycup gumweed	Medicine, Manufacture	resin used for gumming sinew thread for arrow making; in a styptic for wounds
Helianthus annuus L.	common sunflower	Food, Game	seeds for food and cooking oil; flower heads used for pretend war bonnets by boys
Helianthus tuberosus L.	Jerusalem artichoke	Food	tubers used for food, eaten raw or cooked (roasted)
Hesperostipa spartea (Trin.) Barkworth	porcupinegrass	Manufacture	needles used for hairbrushes
Heterotheca villosa (Pursh) Shinners var. *villosa*	hairy false goldenaster	Medicine	tops, leaves, and inflorescences boiled to make a cure for saddle galls on horses
Hierochloe odorata (L.) P. Beauv.	sweetgrass	Perfume	leaves used
Juniperus horizontalis Moench	creeping juniper	Medicine, Incense	used in the same manner as *Juniperus virginiana*
Juniperus virginiana L.	red cedar	Medicine, Incense	remedy for chills and colds
Lactuca tatarica (L.) C.A. Mey.	blue lettuce	Medicine, Child care	for swellings from broken bones; bath sponge or wash rag on children
Liatris spp.	blazing star	Agriculture	indicator species for time to harvest corn
Linum lewisii Pursh	Lewis flax	Medicine	remedy for diarrhea and burns
Lomatium dissectum (Nutt.) Mathias & Constance	bear root	Medicine	burned and the smoke used for an earache
Lonicera dioica L.	limber honeysuckcle	Manufacture	seeds used as noise-makers in rattles
Lophophora williamsii (Lem. ex Salm-Dyck) J.M. Coult.	peyote	Medicine	cermonial plant
Machaeranthera pinnatifida (Hook.) Shinners	lacy tansy aster	Horse care	for reviving an exhausted horse in a chase or war expedition
Maclura pomifera (Raf.) C.K. Schneid.	Osage orange	Manufacture	wood used in making bows

Species Names	Common Name	Type of Use	Uses
Mentha arvensis L.	wild mint	Drink, Medicine	tea; a carminative and remedy for colds, especially chest colds
Mentzelia decapetala (Pursh ex Sims) Urb. & Gilg ex Gilg	tenpetal blazingstar	Craft	paint brush, decorative design
Monarda fistulosa L.	beebalm	Perfume, Medicine	perfume for clothing and hair pomade; tea
Nicotiana quadrivalvis Pursh	indian tobacco	Smoking	leaves used
Opuntia polyacantha Haw.	plains pricklypear	Medicine	to relieve excessive menstrual flow
Parthenocissus vitacea (Knerr) Hitchc.	woodbine	Manufacture	seeds used as noise-makers in rattles
Pediomelum esculentum (Pursh) Rydb.	tipsin	Food	starchy root, important food source
Phragmites australis (Cav.) Trin. ex Steud.	common reed	Craft	adults and children cut them to make beads. Children used for whistles
Physalis heterophylla Nees	clammy groundcherry	Food	collected and eaten by children
Picea glauca (Moench) Voss	white spruce	Perfume, Craft	resin used as adhesive
Pinus ponderosa Lawson & C. Lawson	ponderosa pine	Incense, Craft	resin used as adhesive
Polygonatum biflorum (Walter) Elliott	Solomon's seal	Craft	seeds used as noisemakers in rattles
Polygonum sp.	smartweed	Craft, Game	used to make a whistle by children
Populus deltoides W. Bartram ex Marshall	cottonwood	Horse food	bark of branches and twigs used for horse feed
Prunus americana Marshall	American plum	Food, Game	eaten fresh and dried
Prunus pumila L. var. *besseyi* (L.H. Bailey) Gleason	western sandcherry	Food, Game	large-sized purple-black cherries, sometimes used in sauce and corn pudding
Prunus virginiana L.	chokecherry	Medicine, Food	fruits for food; remedy for postpartum hemorrhage and excessive menstrual flow
Psoralidium argophyllum (Pursh) J. Grimes	silver-leafed scurfpea	Medicine	headaches, hallucination or dreams of seeing the dead
Psoralidium tenuiflorum (Pursh) Rydb.	slimflower scurfpea	Medicine	remedy for fever in babies
Ratibida columnifera (Nutt.) Wooton & Standl.	upright prairie coneflower	Hunting	seeds scattered over snares to mask human odor
Rhus glabra L.	smooth sumac	Medicine	remedy for rash or other eruptions
Ribes sp.	currants	Food	primarily used fresh
Rosa arkansana Porter	prairie rose	Food and Medicine	insect galls from plant used in remedy for sore throat
Rosa woodsii Lindl.	Woods' rose	Drink	inner bark brewed like tea for a pleasant beverage

Species Names	Common Name	Type of Use	Uses
Rubus idaeus L. subsp. *strigosus* (Michx.) Focke	wild raspberry	Food, Drink	the fruit was used for food, the leaves for tea
Salix spp.	willow	Manufacture	used in roof structures for earth lodges, *Salix exigua* Nutt. used in throwing game by boys
Salix amygdaloides Andersson	peachleaf willow	Basketry	light pliable wood for making baskets
Salix eriocephala Michx.	diamond willow	Cooking	fuel for fires; rack for roasting corn
Salix interior Rowlee	sandbar willow	Medicine, Manufacture	young bark used to treat catfish stings; primary material for fish trap
Sanguinaria canadensis L.	bloodroot	Medicine	root pounded into powder and inserted into nose or mouth to stop nasal or mouth hemorrhaging
Schoenoplectus tabernaemontani (C.C. Gmel.) Palla	softstem bulrush	Manufacture	mat making
Shepherdia argentea (Pursh) Nutt.	buffaloberry	Food, Dye	fruit mashed into cakes and dried like chokecherries; mordant for dye
Smilax herbacea L.	carrion flower	Manufacture	The hard, shining seeds were used to put into rattles
Spartina pectinata Bosc ex Link	slough Grass	Manufacture, Horse food	mat making; hay for horses stored for winter
Sphaeralcea coccinea (Nutt.) Rydb.	scarlet globemallow	Medicine	powdered and made into a paste to stop bleeding
Symphoricarpos occidentalis Hook.	western snowberry	Medicine, Manufacture	berries for sore mouth, or any sore; brush was gathered into bundles for brooms
Thalictrum sp.	meadow rue	Perfume	men used seeds for perfume on clothing, used as a love charm to attract women
Typha latifolia L.	cat-tail	Food, Manufacture, Game	rootstocks used as food; chaffy seeds used for tanning deerskin; leaves and stocks for children's game; down used for sanitary care absorbent padding for infants
Ulmus spp.	elm	Basketry	used for working baskets and tying bundles
Viburnum lentago L.	black haw	Food, Cosmetic	fruit dried then boiled; seed then used by girls for cosmetic purposes to give the appearance of a mole

Species Names	Common Name	Type of Use	Uses
Vitis riparia Michx.	riverbank grape	Food, Game	fruit used fresh, cooked in sauce, or dried; leaves used by girls for a game
Xanthium strumarium L.	sandbur	Medicine	large dry bur used to puncture a person's crooked jaw; powder of root then applied to pricked area
Yucca glauca Nutt.	yucca	Manufacture	root used for tanning and for soap
OTHERS			
Letharia vulpina (L.) Wainio	wolf lichen	Dye	exported for sale to other tribes by Arikara, makes a yellow dye
Calvatia sp.	puffball	Food, Medicine	boiled for food; spores used as talcum powder on infants and styptic for umbilial cord
Ustilago maydis	corn smut	Food	when firm and white, before the maturing of the spores, it was cooked with squash

References Cited

Abel, Annie, ed. 1939. *Tabeau's Narrative of Loisel's Expedition to the Upper Missouri.* University of Oklahoma Press, Norman, OK.

Bailey, V. 1920. Identity of the Bean Mouse of Lewis and Clark. *Journal of Mammalogy* 2:70–72.

Beals, J., S.M. Manson, N.R. Whitesell, P. Spicer, D.K. Novins, and C.M. Mitchell. 2005. Prevalence of DSM-IV Disorders and Attendant Help-seeking in 2 American Indian Reservation Populations. *Arch Gen Psychiatry* 62(1):99–108. DOI:10.1001/archpsyc.62.1.99.

Brackenridge, Henry. 1814. *Views of Louisiana, together with a Journal of a Voyage up the Missouri River, in 1811.* Cramer, Spear and Eichbaum, Pittsburg, PA. (cited in https://user.xmission.com/~drudy/mtman/html/Brackenridge/index.htm. Accessed on January 19, 2018).

Bradbury, J. 1904. *Travels in the Interior of America: In the Years 1809, 1810, and 1811* (Vol. 5). A.H. Clark, Cleveland, OH.

Bull, M.J., and N.T. Plummer. 2014. Part 1: The Human Gut Microbiome in Health and Disease. *Integrative Medicine: A Clinician's Journal* 13(6):17.

Conlon, M.A., and A.R. Bird. 2014. The Impact of Diet and Lifestyle on Gut Microbiota and Human Health. *Nutrients* 7(1):17–44. DOI:10.3390/nu7010017.

Darcy, M. 2017. All You Need to Know About Nutrigenomics Testing. Pathway Genomics [web page]. URL: https://www.pathway.com/blog/all-you-need-to-know-about-nutrigenomics-testing/. Accessed August 28, 2019.

Gilmore, M.R. 1913a. Some Native Nebraska Plants with Their Uses by the Dakota. *Collections of the Nebraska State Historical Society* 17:358–371.

Gilmore, M.R. 1913b. A Study in the Ethnobotany of the Omaha Indians. *Collections of the Nebraska State Historical Society* 17:314–357.

Gilmore, M.R. 1919. The Mescal Society among the Omaha Indians. *Publications of the Nebraska State Historical Society* 19:163–167.

Gilmore, M.R. 1921. Plant Relations in North Dakota. *University of North Dakota Departmental Bulletin* V(2):1–16.

Gilmore, M.R. 1922. Some Comments on "Aboriginal Tobaccos". *American Anthropologist* 24(4):480–481.

Gilmore, M.R. 1924a. The Arikara Fish Trap. *Indian Notes* 1:120–134.

Gilmore, M.R. 1924b. Old Assiniboin Buffalo-Drive in North Dakota. *Indian Notes* 1(4):204–211.

Gilmore, M.R. 1925a. The Ground Bean and Its Uses. *Indian Notes* 2:178–187.

Gilmore, M.R. 1925b. Arikara Basketry. *Indian Notes* 2:89–95.

Gilmore, M.R. 1926a. Arikara Commerce. *Indian Notes* 3:13–18.

Gilmore, M.R. 1926b. Indian Custom of Carrying the Pipe. *Indian Notes* III(2):89–95.

Gilmore, M.R. 1926c. Some Interesting Indian Foods. *Good Health* 61(7):12–14.

Gilmore, M.R. 1927a. Origin of the Arikara Silverberry Drink. *Indian Notes* IV(2):125–127.

Gilmore, M.R. 1927b. The Coyote's Boxelder Knife. *Indian Notes* IV(3):214–216.

Gilmore, M.R. 1927c. Dr. Gilmore's Field Researches in 1926. *Indian Notes* IV(2):166–169.

Gilmore, M.R. 1928. The Cattail Game of Arikara Children. *Indian Notes* 5:316–318.

Gilmore, M.R. 1929. Arikara Account of the Origin of Tobacco and Catching of Eagles. *Indian Notes* VI(1):26–33.

Gilmore, M.R. 1931a. Notes on the Gynecology and Obstetrics of the Arikara Tribe of Indians. *Papers of the Michigan Academy of Science Arts and Letters* 14:71–81.

Gilmore, M.R. 1931b. The Arikara Tribal Temple. *Papers of The Michigan Academy of Science, Arts, and Letters* XIV:47–70.

Gilmore, M.R. 1932. Some Aboriginal Uses of Plants by the Arikara Indians. Unpublished manuscript, Box 1, Melvin R. Gilmore Papers, Bentley Historical Library, University of Michigan, Ann Arbor, MI.

Gilmore, M.R. 1977. *Uses of Plants by the Indians of the Missouri River Region.* University of Nebraska Press, Lincoln, NE (originally Smithsonian Institution, Bureau of American Ethnology Annual Report, vol. 33, 1919).

Gilmore, M.R. 1987. *Prairie Smoke.* University of Minnesota Press, Minneapolis, MN.

Heron, M.P. 2017. Deaths: Leading Causes for 2015. National Vital Statistics Reports, vol. 66, no. 5. Department of Health and Human Services, Washington, DC.

Journals of the Lewis and Clark Expedition [web page]. 2005. University of Nebraska Press/University of Nebraska-Lincoln Libraries-Electronic Text Center. URL: http://lewisandclarkjournals.unl.edu/. Accessed on January 2, 2013.

Kartesz, J.T., The Biota of North America Program (BONAP). 2015. Taxonomic Data Center [web page]. URL: http://www.bonap.net/tdc. Chapel Hill, N.C. [maps generated from Kartesz, J.T. 2015. Floristic Synthesis of North America, Version 1.0. Biota of North America Program (BONAP). (in press)] Accessed on January 10, 2020.

Kindscher, K. 1987. *Edible Wild Plants of the Prairie—an Ethnobotanical Guide.* University Press of Kansas, Lawrence, KS.

Kindscher, K. 1992. *Medicinal Wild Plants of the Prairie—an Ethnobotanical Guide.* University Press of Kansas, Lawrence, KS.

Kindscher, K., ed. 2016. *Echinacea: Herbal Medicine with a Wild History.* Springer, Switzerland.

Kindscher, K., L. Martin, S. Corbett, and D. Lafond. 2018. Nutritional Properties of Native Plants and Traditional Foods from the Central United States. *Ethnobiology Letters* 9(2):214–227.

Lallanilla, M. 2005. Eating Dirt: It Might be Good for You [web page]. URL: http://abcnews.go.com/Health/Diet/story?id=1167623&page=1. Accessed on October 30, 2019.

Lewis, M., W. Clark, and Members of the Corps of Discovery. 2002. Journal entry from September 4, 1806; also October 11, 1804. In *The Journals of the Lewis and Clark Expedition,* edited by G. Moulton. University of Nebraska Press, Lincoln. Retrieved November 15, 2015, from the University of Nebraska Press / University of Nebraska-Lincoln Libraries-Electronic Text Center, The Journals of the Lewis and Clark Expedition web site: http://lewisandclarkjournals.unl.edu/read/?_xmlsrc=lc.toc.xml&_xslsrc=LCstyles.xsl

Melvin R. Gilmore Papers, Bentley Historical Library, University of Michigan, Ann Arbor. Accessed November 2013, September 2014, April 2017.

Parks, D.R. 1970–1997. Arikara Language Documentation Notebooks. Unpublished. American Indian Studies Research Institute, Indiana University, Bloomington, IN.

Parks, D.R. 1991a. *Traditional Narratives of the Arikara Indians: Stories of Alfred Morsette.* University of Nebraska Press, Lincoln, NE.

Parks, D.R. 1991b. *Traditional Narratives of the Arikara Indians: Stories of Alfred Morsette, English translations.* University of Nebraska Press, Lincoln, NE.

Parks, D.R. 2001. Arikara. In *Handbook of North American Indians, Volume 13: Plains*, edited by Raymond J. DeMallie, pp. 365–390. Smithsonian Institution, Washington, D.C.

Phillips, C.M., E. Gesse-Guyot, R. McManus, S. Hercberg, D. Lairon, R. Planells, and H.M. Roche. 2012. High Dietary Saturated Fat Intake Accentuates Obesity Risk Associated with Fat Mass and Obesity-Associated Gene in Adults. *Journal of Nutrition* 142(5):824–831.

Rogers, J. Daniel. 1990. *Objects of Change: The Archaeology and History of Arikara Contact with Europeans.* Smithsonian Institution Press, Washington, D.C.

United States Derpartment of Agriculture, Natural Resources Conservation Service (USDA, NRCS). 2019. The PLANTS Database [web page]. URL: http://plants.usda.gov. Accessed on June10, 2019.

Vangay, P., A.J. Johnson, T.L. Ward, G.A. Al-Ghalith, R.R. Shields-Cutler B.M. Hillmann, S.K. Lucas, L.K. Beura, E.A. Thompson, L.M. Till, R. Batres, B. Paw, S.L. Pergament, P. Saenyakul, M. Xiong, A.D. Kim, G. Kim, D. Masopust, E.C. Martens, C. Angkurawaranon, R. McGready, P.C. Kashyap, K.A. Culhane-Pera, and D. Knights. 2018. US Immigration Westernizes the Human Gut Microbiome. *Cell* 175(4):962–972.

Volney H. Jones Papers, Bentley Historical Library, University of Michigan, Ann Arbor. Accessed September 2014, April 2017.

Will Family Papers, State Historical Society of North Dakota, Bismarck, ND. Accessed September 2014, June 2017.

Young, S.L. 2010. Pica in Pregnancy: New Ideas About An Old Condition. *Annual Review of Nutrition* 30:403–422.

Young, S.L. 2011.*Craving Earth: Understanding Pica, the Urge to Eat Clay, Starch, Ice, and Chalk.* Columbia University Press, New York.

Young, S.L., P.W. Sherman, J.B. Lucks, and G.H. Pelto. 2011. Why on Earth?: Evaluating Hypotheses about the Physiological Functions of Human Geophagy. *The Quarterly Review of Biology* 86(2):97–120.

About the Authors

Kelly Kindscher is a Professor in the Environmental Studies Program and Senior Scientist at the Kansas Biological Survey at the University of Kansas. He is best known as a passionate advocate for native plants, native landscapes and wild places, and his research and publications have focused on ethnobotany, medicinal plants, prairies and prairie restoration, wetlands, and plant communities. He has extensive fieldwork experience, led many research projects, been involved in numerous plant and habitat inventories, restoration projects with native plants. He is the author of the books: *Edible Wild Plants of the Prairie* (1987), *Medicinal Wild Plants of the Prairie* (1992), and most recently editor/author of *Echinacea—Herbal Medicine with a Wild History* (2016). Dr. Kindscher is one of the founders and board member of the Kansas Land Trust, and is on the Advisory Board of the United Plant Savers, the organization focused on the conservation of medicinal plants in the U.S.

Logan Sutton is a Research Associate with the American Indian Studies Research Institute (AISRI) at Indiana University and Language Material Developer with the Culture and Language Department of the Mandan-Hidatsa-Arikara (MHA) Nation. He has a Ph.D. in Linguistics from the University of New Mexico, specializing in the Caddoan languages of the Great Plains—with an emphasis in Arikara and Pawnee—and in the Tanoan languages of the New Mexican Pueblos. He has been actively engaged in varying roles on language documentation, description, and revitalization projects among these communities since 2006. He served for years as primary curator of the Arikara language dictionary database under Dr. Douglas Parks and, since 2015, has served as an Arikara language consultant in various endeavors, most notably in service of MHA Nation Tribal language programs. He currently resides in White Shield, North Dakota on the Fort Berthold Reservation.

Loren Yellow Bird, Sr. is an Arikara historian, traditionalist, and member of the Sahnish (Arikara) Nation. He holds a Bachelor's degree in History and Anthropology from North Dakota State University and is a U.S. Navy veteran. Mr. Yellow Bird is published in various articles, including, *The Journal of Shamanism, Plains Anthropologist,* and *Wicazo Sa Review.* He has served as a subject matter expert in several articles and film documentaries. Loren has been active with the MHA Nation in helping to identify historical locations of uncovered human remains and has worked to help facilitate recovery and traditional burial practices of the Sahnish. He was the technical advisor for the 2016 Oscar winning film, "The Revenant", where he advised actor Leonardo DiCaprio and Director Alejandro Gonzalez Iñárritu. Loren was the 2017 North Dakota Governor's award winner for Frontline employees in Tourism. He has a documentary forthcoming by a French film crew on Sahnish and Northern Plains tribes' connections to horses.

Michael Yellow Bird is Dean and Professor of the Faculty of Social Work at the University of Manitoba. He is a member of the MHA Nation (Mandan, Hidatsa, and Arikara) in North Dakota, USA. He has held faculty appointments at the University of British Columbia, University of Kansas, Arizona State University, Humboldt State University, and North Dakota State University. His research focuses on the effects of colonization and methods of decolonization, ancestral health, Indigenous mindfulness and contemplative practices, and the cultural significance of Rez dogs. He is the author of numerous scholarly articles, book chapters, research reports, and the co-editor of four books: *For Indigenous Eyes Only: The Decolonization Handbook* (2005), *For Indigenous Minds Only: A Decolonization Handbook* (2012), *Indigenous Social Work around the World: Towards Culturally Relevant Education and Practice* (2008), and *Decolonizing Social Work* (2013). He is the co-author of the forthcoming book, *Decolonizing Holistic Pathways Towards Integrative Healing in Social Work.*

CPSIA information can be obtained
at www.ICGtesting.com
Printed in the USA
LVHW071543280921
698929LV00002B/24